THE ROAD TO REASON

Also by
LECOMTE DU NOÜY

Equilibres Superficiels des Solutions Colloïdales
Masson & Cie., Paris, 1929.

Méthodes Physiques en Biologie et en Médecine
Lib. J. B. Baillière, Paris, 1933.

La Temperature Critique du Serum
Hermann & Cie., Paris, 1936.

Le Temps et la Vie
Gallimard, Paris, 1936.

L'Homme devant la Science
Flammarion, Paris, 1939; new ed., 1948.

L'Avenir de l'Esprit
Gallimard, Paris, 1941; new ed., 1948.

La Dignité Humaine
Brentano, New York, 1941; new ed., Paris, 1948.

Surface Equilibria of Colloids
Chemical Catalog Co., Reinhold Pub. Corp., New York, 1926.

Biological Time
Methuen & Co., London, 1936; The Macmillan Co., New York, 1937.

Studies in Bio-Physics: The Critical Temperature of Serum
Reinhold Pub. Corp., New York, 1945.

Human Destiny
Longmans Green & Co., Inc., New York, 1947.

LECOMTE DU NOÜY

THE ROAD TO REASON

BY

Lecomte du Noüy

❧

TRANSLATED AND EDITED BY

Mary Lecomte du Noüy

LONGMANS, GREEN AND CO.

New York · Toronto

1948

LONGMANS, GREEN AND CO., INC.
55 FIFTH AVENUE, NEW YORK 3

LONGMANS, GREEN AND CO.
215 VICTORIA STREET, TORONTO 1

THE ROAD TO REASON

FIRST EDITION

Printed in the United States of America
Montauk Book Mfg. Co., Inc., N. Y.

To

MAY LECOMTE DU NOÜY

In memory of the Grand Canyon where this book was written, in gratitude for her collaboration and encouragement, and with all my love.

P. L. N.

PREFACE

FOR THE hundreds of thousands of persons who have read Lecomte du Noüy's *Human Destiny* with sympathy, understanding, and help to themselves, no introduction to *The Road to Reason* is necessary. For such readers, the present volume—written some seven years earlier—offers a fuller comprehension of Dr. du Noüy's scientific outlook and of those aspects of modern scientific thought that seemed to him most significant. For those who have not yet read *Human Destiny*, *The Road to Reason* provides the proper introduction to that final expression of Du Noüy's fundamental concern with the meaning of human life.

As one of the first to apply sound physical training and outlook to problems of biology, he was in the very forefront of that shift in interest from the inanimate to the problems of life that marks the science of our generation. His own scientific work dealt first with the healing of wounds and then, for the major part of his life, with the application of physical chemistry to problems of biology. During World War I, he showed that it was possible to calculate the time required for a sterile wound to heal. Besides giving for the first time information essential to proper planning of hospital facilities, these experiments were the source of the ideas on time expressed in his book *Biological Time*, published successively in France, England, and America.

The last twenty years of his scientific life were spent investigating protein solutions and blood serum. His classical work on the spreading of proteins on water enabled him to measure in a totally new way the number of these molecules and even their dimensions. He used this same property to demonstrate by physico-chemical means the immune reaction. This success led him to continue his experiments on immunity through the development of other techniques that have thrown much new light on the process underlying all recovery from infectious disease. The instruments devised for these experiments have proved equally valuable in the study of other colloidal systems and are now being extensively used for research work on oils and greases, as well as on numerous biological problems.

The books written in later life show that Du Noüy was far more than a scientific innovator. For him science was not the end in itself but the essential instrument for formulating those problems that must gnaw at the heart of every conscious being: the significance and goal of human existence. Both man's place in nature and his understanding of this place have been altered by the growth of natural science to a degree that we are, in fact, only beginning to appreciate. No one can afford to neglect this impact of science—*and of scientific modes of thought even more than of scientific fact*—upon the future course of humanity. Du Noüy was one of the very few scientists in this generation able to bring his sound scientific knowledge to bear on this fundamental question. The aspects of truth have always been as varied as the personalities of those seeking it, and this is equally true of scientific knowledge. Other scientists would undoubtedly have a different approach to the roots of science; but there is a common goal, and the insight of one serious searcher must carry an important message to every other.

I have deep personal reasons for testifying to the acuity and profound seriousness of Du Noüy's understanding of the impact of science on our world. For over twenty years he was to me that ideal of intimate friend and older brother who, sharing the same basic goal in life, could point out through greater experience the road toward its attainment. His untimely death while at the height of his own creative ability is a tragedy made more profound to some of us through the irreparable personal loss it involves.

Science is a product of the same spirit of adventure that has given our present civilization its special flavor. Scientific knowledge has created much of the great wealth of this civilization, but it is important to realize that science has not arisen from a search for riches, but for understanding. The true pioneers and architects of science have been individuals who have sought to comprehend the physical world in which they found themselves in the same exploring and creative spirit that has since the days of the Renaissance produced so great a stream of innovators. It is essential that society realize the following proposition: science will continue to advance as long, but only as long as it can be the supreme adventure for individuals who find in the need to understand the paramount purpose for living. Du Noüy had this spirit, and what he has written is in essence a record of his personal search for understanding.

A sustained attempt to grow throughout one's whole life is, to say the least, hard to maintain, and most of us need the encouragement and example of those who have succeeded. Du Noüy was such a successful person. He is one of the very few I have known of whom it can be said that every year he was greater, both intellectually and as a human being, than the year before.

Those who have read *Human Destiny* will recognize how much farther his philosophical thought had progressed in the few years that followed the writing of the present book. It scarcely needs to be noted that *The Road to Reason* is not, and was never intended to be, a popularization of scientific facts. As an expression of the evolving ideas of one of the pioneers in extending our truly marvelous physical understanding of the inanimate world to the deeper mystery of the living process, it had a very different object. In America we have no established tradition that encourages and trains a scientist in the extraordinarily difficult business of recording the interplay of his work as technical expert with his outlook as a developing human being. The French have this thoroughly admirable tradition, and we may be thankful that Du Noüy, for all his admiration for and participation in things American, fulfilled his essentially French "obligation" to the society that molded him, and that he in turn could in a measure remake.

RALPH W. G. WYCKOFF

Laboratory of Physical Biology
National Institute of Health
Bethesda, Maryland
October, 1948

ACKNOWLEDGMENT

I wish to acknowledge with pleasure the valuable assistance given me by Mr. J. J. O'Neill of the *New York Herald Tribune* and by Dr. Karl K. Darrow of the Bell Telephone Laboratories. My indebtedness to Dr. Ralph W. G. Wyckoff for his constant help and encouragement is incalculable. I should also like to express my thanks to my publishers for their cooperation.

M. L. N.

New York, N. Y.
October 1, 1948

ACKNOWLEDGEMENT

CONTENTS

Scientific learning is composed of two opposites which nonetheless meet each other. The first is the natural ignorance that is man's lot at birth. The second is represented by those great minds that have investigated all knowledge accumulated by man only to discover at the end that in fact they know nothing. Thus they return to the same fundamental ignorance they had thought to leave. Yet this ignorance they have now discovered is an intellectual achievement. It is those who have departed from their original condition of ignorance but have been incapable of completing the full cycle of learning who offer us a smattering of scientific knowledge and pass sweeping judgments. These are the mischief makers, the false prophets.

—PASCAL

INTRODUCTION

A WRITER should always search his soul and conscience and ask himself whether the book he has in mind is really worth publishing. I am not optimistic enough to believe that this would greatly reduce the literary, philosophic, or scientific output. Too many different elements are involved and their combined importance often eclipses the futility or mediocrity of a work that the author, for evident reasons, is usually tempted to overlook.

Some of these elements have succeeded in stifling my qualms. Many questions have, for years, repeatedly thrust themselves upon me in the calm retreat of the laboratory. Doubts arose in my mind concerning the real significance and relativity of the fruits of human thought; concerning the value of the methods we employ and the deductions we can logically make.

In order to clarify my own ideas, I decided to expound the problem briefly. This task seemed important because the conflict that has arisen is no longer limited to the laboratory. It penetrates into our social life and influences our private life. Apparently, man cannot live without a mystical belief. This is an experimental fact and would not be dangerous in itself if men were pure spirits. The statement that this is not the case will, I think, surprise no one. Some people have a tendency to believe themselves responsible for the happiness of humanity. This tendency is sometimes praiseworthy and is based either on religious faith, which is an unalterable conviction and does not rest on what we call reason, or else on a blind faith in reason and on an exaggerated opinion of their own intelligence and the dangerous pride that results therefrom.* I naturally eliminate those who pursue only their personal interests and who consider all methods and impostures as legitimate.

These two forms of mysticism (the religious and the anti-religious) are strangely alike in their consequences. When we stop to think about it, this is not surprising, for they both flourish in human beings who are identical in other respects and whose means of exteriorization are very similar. Backed by the irrefutable authority of Revelation, some priests tried, in ages past, to silence reason and science, which they instinctively feared, whereas nowadays anti-religious people rely on human intelligence and its creation, science. At any rate, that is their avowed profession of faith.

In the first case we are helpless. We cannot discuss faith. It either exists, or does not exist. Its origin and essence are superhuman. In the second case we have the possibility and the right, by virtue of the rationalistic foundation of this kind of mysticism, to examine its bases critically. The intransigence of religious authority tends to prejudice an independent mind in favor of a positive materialistic rationalism, and its advocates did not fail to use this argument in order to propagate their doctrine. Science is not mysterious, they said. It is open to all. It is democratic and respects truth alone. Everything is aboveboard, science explains all things and what is not yet explained will be

---

* EDITOR'S NOTE: To compare these views and certain others of similar nature expressed in this book with Lecomte du Noüy's later thoughts, the reader is referred to *Human Destiny*.

known in the near future. Human intelligence is infallible and unlimited. Nothing can escape it.

Words such as these evidently fascinate and flatter the masses. When we speak of human intelligence and have in mind a Descartes, a Pascal, a Newton, or a Bergson, every man imagines that we are referring to his own intellect. This misunderstanding threatens to have unfortunate consequences, as the same thing can be said of intelligence as of common sense, which Descartes, with a profound irony unnoticed by most of his commentators, described as "the most equitably distributed thing in the world, *as nobody usually desires more of it than he already possesses.*"

For this reason, and also because of the effects of centuries of religious dictatorship, science at the outset represented liberation. Many educated people followed the 18th century Encyclopedists and thought they showed a scientific spirit by becoming atheists. It was the logical consequence of the intolerance of the Church, which had hoped to consolidate its authority by smothering science under a bushel. This attitude alienated truth-loving, intelligent men, who by their devotion to freedom of thought, based on a sense of human dignity and on their horror of obscurantism, were necessarily opposed to a discipline that imposed the contempt of observed facts.

Today conditions have changed. Science no longer frightens anybody and has won its right to citizenship in the Vatican itself. This is a profound evolution and it was bound to take place. Nowadays, the cultivated man who believes in God seems, by a strange reversal, to be freer in many cases than the militant atheist. No experimental fact, no discovery, can shatter the faith of the true believer. Everything he observes, outside as well as inside of himself, is of divine origin. His faith is not based on science and has nothing to fear from it. Only *human theories* superimposed on facts, and often derived from extrapolations, may sometimes seem dangerous. Experience has shown him that well-observed phenomena endure, and that science has never had to retract an affirmation based on facts that are well established within accurately defined limits. The retractions science has been forced to make do not belong to the experimental field, but *concern the supposed mechanism of the co-ordinated succession of phenomena* and the prediction of the future. Facts remain; human anticipations vanish. In research itself, the believer does not attempt to convince: he is free.

Certain militant atheists, on the contrary, are possessed by a passionate frenzy, somewhat like that of the first Christians, which by its very violence reveals a rational fragility. Others are merely filled with hatred. Peaceful agnosticism would seem to be the wisest attitude, but fears for the immediate future of our civilization have turned the selfish indifference that flourished before the first World War into serious anxiety. A thousand questions arise that cannot be answered. The majority of cultivated people are ignorant of the foundations on which modern philosophical doctrines are based. They only know that, nowadays, these doctrines all pretend to be scientific. What, then, is the actual philosophic and scientific balance sheet of our time? What do we know? What is the value of science? Is science capable of fighting against the lack of moral values? What has it accomplished in the realm of pure knowledge? Behind the material preoccupations of daily life, we sense a painful uncertainty, which this book will certainly not succeed in dissipating entirely, but which it may help to direct into constructive channels.

Revolutionary discoveries have succeeded each other rapidly since the beginning of the 20th century. Many theories that threatened to become dogmas have been challenged in the past fifteen years. This general upheaval has created great confusion but also a certain clarity. Our self-confidence has been somewhat shaken. Everything seems more complicated than we at first thought. We have become more prudent, less affirmative. The very foundations of our science have been attacked; there is a "crisis of determinism."

It seemed to me that the time was ripe for a general, unbiased revision and for a logical criticism of some of our concepts, theories, and reasonings.

A number of scientists and the philosophers of the Vienna Circle try, by purely verbal and symbolic systems, to create rigorous syntactic methods from which all error will be excluded by the very form of the propositions. We will try, on the contrary, to use the scientific fact as our only support and guide. It is the one thing we know that inspires us with confidence. It is, and always will be, indisputable.

We shall, therefore, often be in conflict with the Logisticians and Dialecticians. This does not frighten us, for they are entirely dependent on the research worker. In his penetrating study on logic, Gonseth mercilessly exposed the weaknesses of these philosophies.[1] Personally, I believe that, even if actual scientific discoveries bring us rapidly face to face with great philosophical problems, we shall not solve these problems by syntactical or logistical methods. Some of these efforts, which fascinate us by their ingenuity, are at bottom surprisingly conceited and childish.

[1] F. Gonseth, *Qu'est-ce que la Logique,* Hermann & Cie. Paris, 1937. See also: L. Rougier. Cambridge Congress. (Erkenntnis 1938.)

We shall, therefore, first of all briefly study the objectives of science. In fact, we shall simply try to define. Next, we shall consider the methods employed to interpret the sequence of facts, namely, the methods used to establish human scientific laws. We shall then examine the interpretations, the theories, and finally the points of contact between the material universe and the moral and spiritual world. This will lead us to consider the problem of responsibility.

THE OBJECTIVES OF SCIENCE

_____

Argument

Objects can be perceived only through the intermediary of our senses, and the existence of our universe as *we* see it depends on nerve reactions on which all "normal" beings can agree. A scientific fact could not exist without the receiving instrument, Man, who must, therefore, always be taken into consideration. We shall never know whether this image created by our senses corresponds to reality.

With the help of mathematics we have constructed a universe of atoms and electrons and have formulated laws to explain their actions. But life itself obeys other laws, and science has not been able to bridge the gap between the two. This raises a serious problem.

We know that all matter and energy are discontinuous; yet science is built on faith in the identity of men's reactions and in the continuity of these reactions. Continuity in time, in thought, in movement; continuity of the species, of evolution, exist. What is their source?

What, in fact, is reality?

1

THE OBJECTIVES OF SCIENCE

OBSERVED facts are the only scientific data to work with. Let us first consider the bare facts separately.

I am sitting in front of my table on which a number of objects are placed. I see and recognize them. I characterize the table by its color, hardness, dimensions, and shape, which are revealed to me by my senses, that is to say, by the modification of certain brain cells. In other words, what I call "table" is, in reality, a slight and purely subjective perturbation of my sensory cells. There is no specific difference between the sense impressions that give me an idea of smoothness, of shape—qualities that I project outside of myself and attribute to "this" table—and those that produce the pain I feel when I hit the table violently with my fist. Nevertheless, I recognize this pain as being internal, subjective. I do not consider it as a quality of the table. I only consider as such the properties that can, under ordinary conditions—namely within certain precise limits—produce in my neighbor, whom I suppose to be normal

25

(that is to say, to have similar sensory reactions), impressions that will coincide with mine if we both give an independent description of this table.

The characteristics of the concept of an "object" are obvious: first, a subjective reaction of the sensory organs under well-determined physical conditions—temperature, relative motion of the object, or of the instrument of observation (in the present instance my hand, etc.); second, a necessary control by means of another observation, made under identical conditions by another observer, who must be identical to myself; third, a comparison of the two subjective series of data by means of words and symbols based on previous and similar experiments. I call "hard" a substance that does not give under my fingers; "red" or "green" an impression of the eye that recalls those given me by certain flowers or a lawn.

Under these conditions, I can speak of a table, a flower, a child, and I admit their external objective existence, because my neighbors experience the same sensations at the same moment as I do, and communicate them to me. This is what we call our reality, our universe. Its existence, therefore, depends on nervous reactions on which all "normal" beings—namely, the majority—can agree (abnormal beings, such as Daltonians,* are eliminated).

The following important problem immediately arises. It is as old as the world, and I will only mention it briefly as it has been admirably and originally expounded by Mariani.[1] To what extent does the pictured representation, in the shape of an object, correspond to reality? Every-

---

* EDITOR'S NOTE: After John Dalton, early English philosopher and father of the chemical theory of atoms, who had abnormal vision and was not aware of the fact until he discovered late in life that he was color blind.

[1] Jean Mariani, *Les Limites de la Notion d'objet et d'objectivité*. Hermann & Cie. Paris, 1937.

thing takes place as if a combination of causes responsible for our sensory reactions really existed outside of us. But what analogy is there between this combination of causes and the image of the table that we derive therefrom? What Mariani calls the "principle of subjectivity" is the fact that this image corresponds only approximately to the reality. Accordingly, the essential part of scientific laws can, and must, be stated independently of any particular representation. The positivism of the Viennese School resorts to a subjectivism which replaces scientific ideas by stenographic summaries of experiments. This, however, does not solve or eliminate the problem, which was purely formal and Aristotelian up to the advent of quantum mechanics. In classical physics the concept of objectivity is never separated from the idea of an object that has given it birth. But the quantum theory presents a system in which the "objective" laws of nature *no longer interpret* the objective properties of objects. That is precisely why I shall not dwell on this subject, for I intend to limit myself, temporarily at least, to the realm of macroscopic physics, namely, to our perceptible universe. A determinism exists in this realm of natural objective laws related to phenomena that can be geometrically situated in time and space. We know that this condition is not verified in wave mechanics.

It can therefore be stated that there would be no scientific fact (1) if the receiving instrument—man—had not been in the path of certain radiations or fields of force, (2) if this receiver had been a unique example of its kind, and (3) if the other identical receivers had been incapable of communicating with each other and of comparing their reactions.

This simple observation clearly defines the respective

positions of man and his universe. We try to know the latter so as to be able to foresee the future. Our direct knowledge can only be relative and does not in any way entail an identity between the real universe and the image it creates in our minds. The existence of this identity is, moreover, incidental and will always be impossible to demonstrate. But our intelligence with the help of that amazing mental shorthand, mathematics—the most admirable tool of logic created by man—has led us to conceive a universe whose microscopic foundations *have no apparent link* with the foundations of our macroscopic universe. I use "microscopic" in the sense of sub-atomic and not in the sense of visible under the microscope. The laws are different; determinism no longer seems to exist. We thus face a conflict of fundamental importance.

This duality, which we shall refer to again, is unquestionably the stumbling block of science, or if one prefers, of modern scientific philosophy. It is the "new factor," which has made it possible to reconsider all the old problems, such as causality and even free will, and to examine them under a new light. For it is no longer a question of mere mental gymnastics, but of experimental facts that are as perfectly known, and defined, as those of classical physics. A well-observed and controlled scientific fact cannot be discussed; that is why we can say that facts, and facts alone, constitute the framework of science. Only by multiplying them, and never losing sight of them, can we hope to progress.

Thus, it is impossible to conceive a scientific fact, or a phenomenon, without the presence of man. To speak of a fact existing objectively, per se, is to make the mistake of the man who, on receiving a telegram, thinks that the writing is that of the sender. As Eddington [2] points out, "it is the inexorable law of our acquaintance with the external world that that which is presented for knowing becomes transformed in the process of knowing." It must be borne in mind that this in no way prejudices the "absolute" existence of the fact itself, *whether or not it differs* from our mental image.[3] But we can only experiment and reason on properties revealed by our senses, or by instruments that extend them. If the receiving instrument, man, is indispensable for the transformation of elementary impulses into macroscopic sensory groups, we cannot neglect him. We must take him into account, even though it is not clear how this can be accomplished. To forget him systematically amounts to the same as to forget the radio receiver with all its imperfections, or to neglect the behavior of living membranes in physiology. Evidently, when a biologist seeks a quick approximate answer to a problem, he is authorized to take only well-known physico-chemical forces into account, and to consider either membranes or cell walls as inert elements. But all physiologists know that an artificial membrane does not act like a living one. The osmotic pressure in a living organism does not rigorously obey the same laws as in a Dutrochet osmometer; that is, unless the membrane dies, in which case physico-chemical laws apply. Therefore, even when no reasoning is involved and we are merely dealing with an isolated fact, we must never lose sight of the relativity of this fact in relation to ourselves.

In the second place, I said that an observed fact only

[2] Sir Arthur Eddington, *New Pathways in Science,* University Press, Cambridge, 1935, pp. 4 and 7.
[3] Einstein, "The belief in an external world, independent of the perceiving subject, is the basis of all science." *The World As I See It,* New York, 1934.)

becomes a scientific fact when all the observers are in unanimous agreement. *Faith in identical reactions to identical facts is therefore essential.* Without it, no science is possible, for science is intrinsically universal. It has been said that art is personal and science is universal.[4] Science must be transmitted in order to evolve, and we cannot conceive a stationary science. Therefore, not only confidence in the actual identity of reactions is necessary, but also *faith in the continuity of this identity.* Here we come across an especially curious problem, the notion of continuity, which cannot be separated from man considered as a receiving instrument.

What is the origin of this concept? We can understand its being born in primitive man as, on our scale of observation, the information given by our senses reveals a continuity in all observed phenomena. Spatial continuity: matter in all its manifestations, radiation (light, heat, electricity), forces in general. Temporal continuity: movements, growth, evolution, etc. But the clearness of this concept began to dim as soon as our perfected instruments of observation forced us to admit that the most elementary continuity, that of matter, was only a question of scale. The edge of a razor blade, when seen through a micro-

[4] "L'Art c'est moi—La Science c'est nous." This ideal has manifestly not been attained as yet. At present, even in science, personality, "sympathies," still play a part. Einstein has said that he "dislikes" Eddington's theory although he cannot disprove it. Eddington has said that Einstein's theory is a matter of taste. Poincaré, when speaking of pure mathematics, where it seems reason alone should reign, divided mathematicians into different psychological types and pointed out that a certain kind of reasoning, capable of convincing one type, will never convince another. How would Lord Kelvin, who said he could understand only provided he could imagine a mechanical model, have reacted to the Broglie-Schrödinger electron? Faraday, and later Berthelot, did not accept the atomic theory although, in the opinion of their contemporaries, it was already well established. Whenever there is no objective confirmation, our attitude toward certain theories depends, in the last resort, on aesthetic considerations, disturbing as this may seem.

scope, does not give the same picture of a straight line that it does when seen by the naked eye; it looks much more like the coast of Maine on a large-scale map. When we carry the analysis further and, abandoning the support furnished by the direct examination of the fact, consider concepts deduced from experiments, we arrive at molecules, atoms, and electrons. At this stage we definitely lose contact, not only with the continuity of the edge of the razor blade, but with that of the steel itself, and of matter in general. As Eddington put it,[5] "Instead of being solid substance my desk is more like a swarm of gnats." Nevertheless, the notion persists and is indispensable to us in spite of the fact that, little by little, since the beginning of the 19th century, science has successfully striven to demonstrate the granular nature of all our universe; in other words, to contradict our senses and our common sense.[6]

After matter, it was the turn of electricity to lose its continuous aspect and to present a granular structure; then energy itself (in the form of radiation) became granular through the admirable work of Planck. Here our efforts at mechanical representation or visualization are unavailing. It is impossible for us to conceive energy in the shape of separate elements. No model borrowed from our macroscopic world can represent Planck's constant h. This universal constant, one of the most fundamental in our science, multiplied by the frequency of vibration, gives the energy of the quantum, or energy packet, emitted by an atom.

But even this was not sufficient. Louis de Broglie, followed by Schrödinger, and many others, granularizes light itself and revives Newton's old emission theory in a more

---

[5] Sir Arthur Eddington, *loc. cit.*, p. 1.

[6] We can unfortunately no longer, like Huxley, consider science as "organized common sense."

complicated form without, however, destroying the wave theory. We are amazed by all this intelligence and genius; amazed, but not quite satisfied. For, in spite of everything, continuity exists, if not in matter and energy, at least in time.[7] Can the concept "scale of observation" alone explain it? In other words, is continuity only a property superimposed by man on the discontinuity of facts, because of his imperfect sensory nerve system or of a specific contingency of his brain? Is continuity always a subjective illusion, as purple is a mixture of blue and red; and the softness of velvet, or of a baby's skin, the consequence of the incapacity of our fingers to separate individual actions? One can understand that the coarseness of the receiving instrument should round out the angles, fill in the gaps and give us a false impression of material continuity, just as a baker's scale is incapable of registering milligrams. But the continuity of time, of movement, the continuity of the species, of the growth of a tree, of the anthill and the hive, of evolution, of memory, of thought; what are their origins? The nature of this "evolutive" continuity seems to differ from that of the *static continuum* that can be explained by the infirmity of our senses. The direction of evolution, in all evolving material systems, is given solely by the consideration of the concept of entropy. We shall see, farther on, that the application of this concept to living phenomena has not yet been realized and raises grave difficulties of principle. Must we admit that, in all cases, the notion of evolutive continuity has no counterpart in the objective universe? This is the thesis of the pure materialist and is far from being actually proved. It is difficult to see how he will solve the problem, when evolution results in an

[7] This statement can in itself be criticized, as we cannot separate matter from time; but we shall overlook this point for the moment.

increase in complexity, in apparent contradiction to the
increase of entropy.

Our science is the result of the effort made by our intelligence to correct the imperfections of our senses. But we
must not forget that some day we will be compelled to link
up this intelligence, by a relation of cause to effect, to the
corpuscular world, entirely ruled by chance, that issued
from it.

Where does this intuitive concept of continuity come
from? How is it that we can speak of "Man" as Borel
does?[8] ". . . This platonic maxim signifies that the God
who governs the universe has a mind resembling that of
the geometers, and that the latter, therefore, can succeed
in penetrating the divine and immutable laws of the world.
From the day man understood that he could set himself
such a goal he has never let himself be turned aside from
it. Even in history's darkest periods, when material worries
absorbed almost all his energy, knights errant of reason
maintained and transmitted the torch of antique thought."
It is inconceivable that this continuity should be entirely
determined by discontinuous mosaic phenomena, for it
requires a link, an element transmitted from one discontinuous granular phenomenon to another; and what
could be the nature of this element?

Continuity, therefore, appears on a superior scale. But
how? Is it, or is it not, contained in the individual constitutive elements? If thought is entirely the result of purely discontinuous physico-chemical phenomena—epiphenomenal consciousness—it must, in the last analysis, be itself
discontinuous, and its continuity is of the same order as
statistical continuity. A philosopher might ask himself if
thought is not the only form of continuous energy. For how

[8] E. Borel, *Le Hasard,* 2nd ed., p. 4.

can we imagine discontinuity if not by means of continuity? Thus we see how the most precise scientific question when it lacks experimental data can, if we are so minded, lead us down the slippery incline of metaphysics.

The important fact to be remembered in the foregoing lines is that to construct human science—and for us there is no other—we can in no case ignore man and his sensory nerve system, which condition this science. All scientific data necessarily embody an element that we tend to neglect: the human factor. We neglect it because we admit that there is an identity of structure in human beings, which amounts to an identity of reaction. In the same way we overlook the action of temperature, in certain experiments that are made at constant temperature, or time, in others that are "instantaneous," or in which we simply postulate that the action of time is negligible—in relation to the sensitivity of the recording instruments—because the phenomenon evolves in a relatively short space of time. But we are inclined to forget that these factors have only been *neglected* in these exceptional cases, and that it is sometimes necessary to take them into account. In the same way it matters little if we ignore Einstein's theory, or the absence of parallelism between two plumb lines when we deal with objects on our scale of observation. But this realm is very restricted in comparison to the universe and it is important to remember this fact when we seek to overstep its boundaries, and when we attempt to extrapolate.

* * *

Science is essentially based on the strange need for unification that characterizes the human mind. The goal of science is to understand and to foresee. The scientific method to achieve this consists in breaking up a complex phenomenon into simple elements, and these, in turn, into still simpler ones, until we finally come to one or several phenomena incapable of being further reduced and which are so familiar that their explanation appears evident (criterion of Descartes). Nowadays, this "analysis" unfortunately leads to elements that are totally incomprehensible, because they belong to a realm that seems to be ruled by laws different from those governing our macroscopic world. This criterion therefore is no longer valid. The "evidence" of Descartes has vanished, as did Huxley's "organized common sense."

The process of analysis is, often wrongly, supposed to entail the explanation of the mechanism of coordination in time, that is to say, the evident passage from one phenomenon to another. In a following chapter we shall come back to this subject, and to the problem it raises.

We often make the mistake of believing that we understand this coordination when, instead of comprehending, we simply anticipate it by means of different artifices, such as mathematics. This is false, but we are willing to content ourselves with the illusion. This fallacy is, unfortunately, very frequent. The meaning of the word "comprehend" has changed in the last few years. We are no longer very sure that we will ever comprehend, in the old sense of the word; we must satisfy ourselves with the hope of being able to anticipate, and only within rather narrow limits of time when compared to sidereal, or even geological, durations. In the past we thought we understood when we had simply succeeded in finding an analogous, mechanical model. More often, we said we understood when we had reduced facts to elements so familiar that we mistakenly imagined we knew them. It was the age of innocence. With the exception of a few simple-minded people, who should perhaps be envied, we no longer harbor such illusions.

We know now that no conceivable mechanical model is identical to the mechanism of the atom. We know that Louis de Broglie "forbids" any comparison of this kind. It is virtually an interdiction to "understand." We must admit that we were overoptimistic, for even before wave mechanics the number of phenomena we understood was not very great. In current everyday life, we are easily satisfied by childish pseudo explanations. Man does not so much want to understand as to believe he understands. Here again he confuses reason with sentiment, but curiously enough he always prides himself more on his reason, no matter how little he has of it.

If only we could say that comprehension establishes a link between men. Except, however, for a small elite who speak the same language, this is not the case because, according to their culture and their intelligence, men give different meanings to the word "comprehend." An explanation that will satisfy one man will seem quite inadequate to another. We have seen that this applies to even the greatest minds. Most people content themselves with "word explanations." It is only at a superior degree of intellectual development that we exact more. One day I asked my barber why he always passed his razor blade over his hand after having sharpened it on the leather. "So as to take off the wire edge," he answered. I asked him what the wire edge was and why he had to take it off. He could not answer, and I saw that I had offended him. The explanation he had given me amply satisfied him and he thought it should suffice. Many people are happy with the knowledge that they "take off the wire edge."

In brief, we repeat that the true goal of science is to

anticipate, since we cannot scientifically affirm that some day we will comprehend everything without considerably restricting the meaning of the word "comprehend," and that the basis of all science is faith in the continuity and harmonious sequence of phenomena. Without this confidence in what we call the order of nature, which, as we shall soon see, rests on absolute disorder, our human laws would no longer make sense. Indeed, they are but the expression of this confidence, which can be stated in the following manner: *When we have experimentally observed that certain phenomena are always followed by certain others that seem to be invariably linked to the first by a relation of cause to effect, we word this observation in such a way that it enables us to foresee the second set of phenomena qualitatively, and sometimes quantitatively, whenever the first are present.*

Our scientific laws are always *a posteriori* and governed by the facts to which they must submit, in opposition to what takes place in social laws. But, like the latter, they are relative to the thinking—recording—instrument, man, and merely express the relation, or a series of relations, between him and the external cause. They only describe the succession of psychological states determined in us by these causes. They are, therefore, essentially relative and subjective, and their validity, strictly limited to man, depends on the identity of the reactions of other individuals to the same external stimuli.

It is therefore evident that the meaning of certain expressions, such as "scientific truth," can only be taken in a very restricted sense, and not literally as the public so often does. There is no "scientific truth" in the absolute sense. *Ad veritatem per scientiam* is an absurdity. There are only certain groups of sensations that, in our experience, have always succeeded each other in the same order and that we believe should identically succeed each other in a limited future. This is the essence of our scientific truth. As long as we ignore the relations that unite a physico-chemical phenomenon to the vital and psychic phenomena that can accompany it in a living organism, we cannot say that we thoroughly understand its significance.

What meaning must we then give to the words: truth, reality? Descartes in his first principle decides "never to accept anything as true, which I did not clearly know to be such; that is to say, carefully to avoid precipitancy and prejudice and to comprise nothing more in my judgment than was presented to my mind so clearly and distinctly as to exclude any ground of doubt." This ancient rule is essentially relative to man and leaves no room for a truth devoid of evidence, clearness, and distinctness. Commentators have dwelt at length on these criteria, which nowadays seem inadequate.

Their weaknesses were pointed out as early as the 17th century by an Italian philosopher, Giovanni Battista Vico. He thought Descartes was mistaken when, struck by the certainty of mathematical reasoning, he placed the criterion of truth in individual common sense. If mathematics attains the truth, said Vico, it is because the mind creates mathematics. The criterion of truth, therefore, consists in being created: *what man creates is true for man.* Consequently, only that which is created by the mind is comprehensible. It follows that the universe is incomprehensible, as the mind did not create it.

"To know," said Vico, "is to know through the causes. We can know the causes of mathematics, as their causes are in us. But we are ignorant of the causes of natural phenomena; we can, therefore, neither know, nor comprehend them. To know the universe would be to have created it. Therefore, God alone possesses this knowledge. We can only be conscious of it."

Contrary to what Descartes thought, the criterion of evidence only gives us consciousness and not science. Thus, the existence of thought, which he considers as the first truth which it is impossible to doubt, depends only on consciousness, and in no way on science.

From a philosophical point of view only two truths therefore can classically exist: revealed, divine truth, which is by definition absolute and unverifiable, and scientific truth, which is essentially human and relative. The first totally escapes the objective control of intelligence and reason. We either admit it or do not admit it. The second, on the contrary, represents the very goal of science, the end toward which all the efforts of human intelligence tend.

We can give two different definitions of "reality." For instance, we can say that reality characterizes objects, which are the undisputed existing sources of subjective reactions. Or else we can say that reality is the result of the conjunction of space and time. (We might as well say that it is the result of movement, as movement requires both time and space.) The two definitions are equivalent. Indeed, matter is actually considered as a form of energy. Mass, which is a fundamental property of matter, is a function of the velocity, that is to say, of time and space, inasmuch as a velocity is expressed as the quotient of a length by a time.

Are these two definitions entirely satisfactory and adequate? Do they correspond, as all good definitions should, *toto definito et uni definito* (to all the defined and nothing but the defined)? This is not certain. Scientifically it is so, but if we take a more complex object of a higher order, Pascal for example, shall we say that his reality consisted in his physical body of flesh and puny ailing nerves, or in that which was immaterial in him, in his thought, more alive than ever, in the image we create of him in our minds, and in his influence on men? What does the name Pascal evoke—the frail body or his immortal but imponderable works? Reality often takes on these two aspects in relation to man, and the purely material aspect may be by far the least important, if only because of its ephemeral existence.

Finally, to establish the link between scientific truth and reality we shall say that the former can only be based on the correspondence of the theory—the human explanation of the sequence of phenomena—to the experiment, or to reality. Unfortunately, from our standpoint, we can introduce only quantitative concepts, the only ones with which science is concerned. This imposes a tremendous restriction in the choice of the elements to be singled out from the sum of elements in an experiment. It is not for us to decide whether all the others are illusory.

*   *   *

To achieve its ends, namely the prediction of events in the immediate future, science disposes first of plain experimental facts: matter, electric fields, gravitation, light, living beings, etc. By immediate future I mean a future in which actual conditions will not be so altered as to make observation by man impossible.[9]

[9] This may mean periods of the order of 10 or a 100 million years, but probably not of the order of a billion.

In the second place, it disposes of directly observable processes: radioactive disintegration, fermentation, metamorphosis of insects, development of living beings in general, etc.

By applying the pre-eminently scientific method of analysis, thanks to the peculiar genius of man manifested by inductive and abstractive powers, science has been led to imagine individual entities whose existence was, occasionally, experimentally verified *solely by their effects*. For example, the trajectories of elementary particles (electrons, protons, nuclei), in C. T. R. Wilson's expansion chamber. These entities are the bricks we must use to reconstruct the whole. They only manifest themselves by the *statistical macroscopical effects* that they entail (trajectories, scintillation of Crookes' fluorescent screen, Geiger counter). The more complex atoms and molecules, entities of the second order, cannot yet be observed individually, even by their effects.[10] On a still higher scale, we find the living cells and we can, perhaps, consider certain large molecules as intermediary entities, those of some proteins for example (soluble ferments, Northrop's pepsin and trypsin, viruses of plants and animals isolated by Wyckoff and Stanley).

Science establishes what we call laws to express briefly the temporal sequence of phenomena that are often complicated. By these laws we are enabled to predict the future. They are all founded on a principle that we have to admit blindly, the principle of causality, namely, that

[10] The new electronic microscopes, which already magnify more than 20,000 times, will perhaps soon enable us to "see" certain large organic molecules.

EDITOR'S NOTE: This prediction has since been verified by the experiments of Dr. Ralph W. Wyckoff, who has recently published photographs of numerous protein molecules.

there is no effect without cause and that the same causes always produce the same effects.

The principle of causality raises numerous problems, as we shall see in the following chapters. Its only justification may be that we are in the habit of thinking "causally." The question has become acute since statistical physics replaced the old unalloyed deterministic physics, and especially since the evolution of wave mechanics and the discovery of the principle of indeterminacy. A duality of the natural laws is hardly probable. If, on the one hand, we have absolute, real laws in the realm of (sub-atomic) particles, how is it that the regularity, which we everywhere observe, is entirely governed by statistical laws? If, on the other hand, we admit the reality and the absolute value of the laws dominating our macroscopic universe, how is it that the elements, which constitute objects, are governed only by chance? This conflict struck Schrödinger, who writes: "Clear and definite intelligibility in the world of outer appearances, and behind this a dark, eternally unintelligible imperative, a mysterious Kismet! The possibility that this may be in reality the case must be admitted; but this duplication of natural law so closely resembles the animistic duplication of natural objects that I cannot regard it as at all tenable." [11]

There is a hierarchy in scientific laws. At the very top we have the principles, or general laws, to which no exceptions have ever yet been found. They are the laws of the conservation of energy, or the first principle of thermodynamics; the second principle of thermodynamics, or

[11] E. Schrödinger, *Science and the Human Temperament*, Norton & Co., New York, p. 145. It is interesting to note the tone of these lines. It is characteristic of the new attitude of great physicists toward the universe. Nothing similar exists in the scientific literature of only twenty years ago. The personal, sentimental reaction appears.

Carnot-Clausius' law; Fermat's law, Hamilton's principle of least action, etc. It is evident that in classical optics, for instance, Fermat's principle, which specifies that the path of light is that which takes the least time, is much more general than all the specific optical laws (laws of refraction, of reflection, etc.), which must all obey this principle. The principles and the great general laws express the mysterious harmony of the universe, which may only exist in our consciousness. Man has formulated them painfully, but the real world was always at hand and enabled him to control, experimentally, the generality of these laws. However, a final stage exists, a final "object" of science, which escapes experimental control and is vaster than the principles; it is what, for lack of a better word, we can call the evolutionary concepts, typified by the concept of entropy. In the course of the following chapters we shall have occasion to speak of it at greater length.

THE METHODS OF SCIENCE

Argument

When we wish to understand a mechanism we take it to pieces. In the same way, science analyzes a complicated phenomenon and breaks it down into simpler elements. This often introduces a change in the scale of observation. Unknowingly, we cross a threshold that resembles a one-way turnstile and we cannot retrace our steps.

Science is still divided into almost completely isolated compartments. Unity is a seductive dream—only centuries of experimental research can tell us if it corresponds to reality.

By arbitrarily isolating phenomena, we give them a beginning and an end. Yet phenomena are no more isolated in nature than are notes isolated in a melody. In relation to the evolution of the universe, life is not a beginning and death is not an end.

2

THE METHODS OF SCIENCE

> "I am afraid that there is something empirical in
> the French mind, and that the only way to make
> it admit a truth, is to present this truth as an ex-
> perimental fact."
> —JULES LACHELIER
> Letter to Paul Janet—May 15, 1885

ANALYSIS is the outstanding scientific method. The com-
plementary method, synthesis, can be used in a limited
number of other cases, but has given important results
only in chemistry.

If we want to understand a mechanism, even in a limited sense, we must take it to pieces. To comprehend a
complex phenomenon, we must analyze it (that is, dissect
it) in the hope of discovering the simpler and better-known
phenomena that condition the principal phenomenon.

When dealing with an elementary phenomenon, which
is difficult or impossible to analyze, we restrict ourselves to
studying its behavior as a function of the different conditions capable of influencing it, and to expressing, first
quantitatively, then symbolically by means of a mathemati-

47

cal formula, the relations existing between its variations and those of different parameters; time, temperature, pressure, etc. An isolated observation, according to R. S. Lacape,[1] is "a cross section through the dimension: time."

For instance, in the case of a falling body, the distances covered are measured as a function of time, at all points of the fall *in vacuo*. The resulting figures enable us to enunciate a rule *a posteriori*. This rule is called the law of falling bodies. It reveals the manner in which gravitation, a universal force of unknown nature, acts. By increasing the pressure we can establish the restrictions brought to this law by the friction of air.

There are a certain number of elementary phenomena in the universe that cannot be simplified experimentally and reduced to still simpler ones. It is by means of these phenomena that we hope some day to be able to explain all the complex phenomena of nature.

We have already seen that it would be a mistake to think that we always succeed in comprehending a complex phenomenon by dissecting it. We must take the word "comprehend" in its restricted sense (see p. 36). Indeed, on the one hand, the elementary phenomena that we thus reach (gravitation, electrostatic attraction, etc.) still remain very mysterious and only their ubiquity and familiarity give us the impression that we know them. We know them as we know the blind beggar on the street corner. "Habit abolishes strangeness," said Montaigne.

On the other hand, in the process of analysis, we do not always perceive the links that unite the elements, or we destroy them without being conscious of it. Our knowledge is not inevitably complete, even when we can synthesize a

[1] R. S. Lacape. *La notion de liberté et la crise du déterminisme*, Paris. Hermann & Cie, 1935.

chemical substance, for the processes brought into play are generally different and we are often incapable of explaining the mechanism of its formation in nature. For example, it is certain that thyroxin, a hormone produced by the thyroid gland, or adrenalin, which is secreted by the suprarenal glands, both of which can be made synthetically, are not manufactured in the glands by the same processes or reactions as are used in the laboratory, although the end result appears to be the same.

Moreover, even when we have an exact knowledge of the elements of a body we cannot understand or foresee the specific properties of the whole.[2] Actually a large number of these properties are still considered as epiphenomena, and we cannot link them up to any particular element, or to a combination of elements. This is sometimes true of the simplest bodies. There is nothing in the properties of hydrogen or oxygen that enables us to foresee the properties of their combination: water. It can be easily imagined that when we deal with complex molecules, such as those cited above, or such as pepsin, trypsin, or acetylcholine, we have no idea of the origin of their chemical and biological qualities.

We entirely share the aversion of most people for "absolute beginnings"; it is the natural reaction of all scientists. The properties of any substances are undoubtedly the necessary consequence of the assemblage, according to a definite plan, of the atoms that compose it. We have to admit, however, that in an immense number of cases we are confronted by a fact that resembles an absolute beginning. It would seem that this is one of the most important problems of biology in general.

[2] When it is possible to do so, our prevision is entirely empirical, that is to say, based on previous observations and experimental checks.

The solution is not easy, for it is a typical example of what I shall call a "problem of scale." We are disconcerted, and often helpless, whenever such a problem arises in physics, chemistry, or biology. By "problem of scale" I mean a problem concerning which one knows, or thinks one knows, the nature and properties of the elements constituting the whole, and in which the properties of the whole, on a higher scale of observation, are without predictable relation to those of the elements. They seem to fall out of a clear sky.

An example of this can be found in physics, when we pass from the properties of the electron, of Schrödinger's waves of probability, to the properties of the atom. This passage is accompanied by a radical change in the mechanical conceptions that are at the base of the laws describing the two classes of phenomena. Many similar cases are found in chemistry, as we have just seen, and in biology when we pass from the protein molecule to the living cell, and from the living cell to the different organisms. The most confounding of all is the birth of thought.

We will take another example. Let us imagine that a conscientious observer has decided to study the laws governing human societies. After having considered the problem as a whole, he realizes that he knows nothing of man as an individual, and that this knowledge is indispensable. Here he faces the first "problem of scale," and crosses the first threshold irreversibly. For neither mass psychology nor the laws that govern human societies can be deduced from individual psychology.

Like most scientists, though perhaps slightly more naïve, this observer is convinced of the unity of science and he does not doubt that he will discover the causes of man's behavior by studying the human body. Thus, without being aware of it, he crosses a second threshold. Anatomy leads him to physiology and biochemistry, which constitute a third threshold. To understand certain details of biochemistry, or the chemistry of large molecules, he passes on to inorganic chemistry and thus crosses a fourth threshold, as easily as the preceding ones. To be consistent, he not only studies molecules, but atoms, and their elementary corpuscular constituents: electrons, positrons, protons, etc., thus crossing the last threshold. At this point it is impossible for him to retrace his steps by using the inverse method, and in proportion to the road he has traveled, his gains are meager.

Logically, an all-seeing intelligence should be able to proceed from cause to effect as easily as from effect to cause. Practically, this is not the case. Perhaps because we do not, as yet, possess an all-seeing intelligence. Perhaps, also, because we never see the whole problem when analyzing *ad infinitum* by means of rather coarse experimental methods, and because in the process, we destroy precisely the element, or the configuration, that would enable us to explain the passage from the elementary properties to the properties of the whole.

This much is certain: By analyzing and simplifying we often lose sight of the real problem we had first meant to study, and we find ourselves confronted by another, having no apparent link with the first. Every time we pass one of these thresholds, without being aware of it, we are separated from our problem by a one-way barrier, which resembles a paying turnstile, and we cannot take the same road back again.

At present, science is still divided into almost completely isolated compartments. Unity is a seductive dream, and only centuries of experimental research can tell us if it corresponds to reality. But the very existence of these compartments brings us back to a problem we have already mentioned: namely, subjectivism. Indeed, it is only in our consciousness that all these thresholds exist and that all these problems of scale appear. Let us suppose that, by means of chance alone, we have finally reached the sole objective reality, the elementary particles, which in quantum mechanics can only be adequately represented as "waves of probability." (We will see in the following chapter that, according to our present theories, chance and probabilities alone are the foundation of the whole universe including our intelligence.) Even if these corpuscles, electrons and others, are the ultimate constituents of reality, the mathematical interpretation we give of it is purely conceptual. The first contact between our personality and nature, namely, the first subjective reaction, takes place through the *effects* of these corpuscles as a result of individual encounters with more complex elements capable of being perceived directly (molecules of water in C. T. R. Wilson's experiments, fluorescent molecules in Crookes' spinthariscope, droplets of oil in Millikan's experiment), or as a result of the energy radiated by an immense number of them (spectra, Balmer rays, diffraction, etc.). It cannot be stated that the electron itself is a direct result of experiment. It is a cause deduced from certain effects by a very complicated mental process, for the identity between the element that produces the Balmer rays in the spectra and the element that influences the Geiger counter is not evident at first sight.

The contact between man and nature is, therefore, *only established through the intermediary of objects, which no longer belong to the world of corpuscles, and which obey totally different laws.*

From that moment, our knowledge of the universe becomes entirely subjective and the difficulties that arise in connection with the problems of scale are of a subjective order. These problems are fundamental and real, from a scientific point of view. They may not exist from a philosophical point of view, but is it possible to speak of a philosophy that suppresses man? The very idea is absurd.

To solve these problems it therefore seems necessary, as we have already pointed out, to take into account the sensory system of man and to consider it as one of the essential elements of phenomena as, in the absence of a living nervous system, an all-powerful intelligence would perhaps have been unable to deduce, from the available material, the epiphenomena that culminate in man, his thought, and his science.

Without man, the universe has neither shape nor color, just as in the absence of a tuned receiving set, a broadcast of Beethoven's greatest symphony fades into space unheard, without raising an echo outside the room in which it is played. The photons emitted by the sun, which, by their reflection on objects, living beings, trees, flowers, rocks, determine reactions which we call a landscape, are only wave packets, energy quanta. The phenomena of our world, the objects of our knowledge disappear. Nothing remains but a dreary, silent, and obscure universe.

When we speak of a phenomenon, we speak only of an event, or of a succession of events, arbitrarily isolated from the universe whose evolution they share. By isolating a fact in order to study it, we give it a beginning and an end, which are artificial and relative. In relation to the evolution of the universe, birth is not a beginning, and death is not an end. There are no more isolated phenomena in nature than there are isolated notes in a melody. The chemical analysis of a rose petal, the spectral study of its color pigments, are human creations that nature ignores. The germination of a seed represents an immense series of varied phenomena that are on different scales of observation, but that are coordinated and linked to phenomena on a still higher scale of observation, such as the evolution of the plant, the evolution of the species, and the evolution of life on earth. This is true even in the case of phenomena of unorganized matter. As we stated above, whenever a scientist makes an experiment, there is always an element in the phenomenon that he neglects and that is nevertheless its very condition of existence, namely, himself. When he studies a chemical reaction, or any physical manifestation, *the true phenomenon is constituted by the combination, experimenter + reaction* and not by the reaction alone. Every experiment necessitates the deliberate severance of a more or less important number of threads, of links, apparent or not, that connect the considered facts to the whole, and that are its reason for existence. We create the notion of the individual unit for the needs of analysis, but we are incapable of connecting the precisions given us by this unit to the system of which it is a part. When the characteristics of the unit are inferred from a statistical consideration of the whole (atom, molecule), the immediate problem does not exist on this scale of observation. But when the unit can be isolated (cell, organism), the problem remains whole. How is it, for instance, that we consider a living organism as a unity in itself, and not as the simple sum of its constituents? Certain schools of philosophy have attempted to study it only from this aspect, but this is a rather elementary point of view that eventually leads to more problems than it can solve, and to insurmountable difficulties.

Man is the measure of all things, said the Greeks. He is more than that; he is the origin of all things. Indeed, either the word "thing" expresses every object, every phenomenon directly perceived by the senses, with the exception of ultimate corpuscles (which, in our hypothesis, we admitted as having an absolute objective reality) or these corpuscles are themselves part of a whole, even though they escape direct observation and analysis as isolated units.

In the first case, man is the origin of his universe as he visualizes it, for his own internal reactions are a constitutive part of the phenomena he observes and studies (hypothesis of an absolute objective reality). In the second case, he is still the origin, for it is he himself who imagines that all nature is based on "waves of probability" having no properties in common with the universe he created in his brain (no absolute objective reality).

In the next chapter we shall see the difficulties that arise in trying to explain how nature, starting from a chaotic world of corpuscles, succeeded by chance alone in creating a brain capable of trying to understand its own spontaneous creation.

*   *   *

Analysis, the only practical method we possess, does not then lead us very far toward an intimate knowledge of phenomena. It often takes us away from the main problem, without our being aware of it, and places us in front of others to which it cannot be applied because of experimental difficulties or impossibilities. In such a case it is sometimes possible to infer from previous data that the harmonious sequence, which has been experimentally established up to that point, persists beyond the attained limits, by virtue of a hypothetical continuity.

When the experimental difficulty is not absolute and depends only on ourselves, in other words, when we shrink from making a long series of measurements that should give us numerous points on a curve in cartesian coordinates, as a function of two parameters, we interpolate. In doing this we assume that the law that governs the phenomenon as a function of one of the parameters—time, for example—applies identically between the two experimental points to each value of the abscissa.

This process implies faith in the continuity of the phenomenon between the two points considered. Such a continuity can only be of a statistical nature, inasmuch as we attribute a discontinuous structure to nature.

Though infinitely less dangerous than extrapolation, interpolation sometimes leads to grave errors. For instance, when establishing a curve representing the absorption of light by a substance, if two experimental points are close, one is inclined to connect them by such a curve as is well fitted to the preceding and the following points. And it sometimes happens that, by making an additional measurement, or by using a more refined technique, a critical point, a minimum or a maximum, can be discovered between these two points.

The real danger, however, lies in extrapolation, where the curve is supported experimentally on one side only. This implies not only faith in the continuity but also in the validity of the relations expressed by the equation of the curve, beyond the limits of the experiment.

Now we shall see in the next chapter that the only continuity we can rely on is the continuity derived from statistical considerations, and from the second principle of thermodynamics. But we shall also discover that though this principle may be adequate for the inorganic world, we come up against grave difficulties when we try to apply it to biology.

We must not forget that a scientific law expresses nothing but the successive states of consciousness that are the result of certain external causes, and that we only know these causes indirectly by the subjective reactions they determine. To extrapolate, therefore, is automatically to introduce a new human element, which from the very fact that the experimental control can no longer be obtained *by the same techniques,* transposes the objective phenomenon into a different qualitative plane. This may sound rather obscure, and I shall try to explain it by means of an example.

The world is revealed to us principally by electromagnetic waves, sound waves, gravitation, inertia. Let us momentarily neglect the last three modes, and confine ourselves to the electromagnetic waves. We are surrounded by them. In themselves, considered independently of the presence of man, they can be distinguished from one another only by their wave lengths, which range from those of gamma rays shorter than one billionth of a millimeter in length (a millimeter is about 1/25 of an inch), to those of radio waves, which are several kilometers long (a kilometer is about 6/10 of a mile). These rays are:

the gamma rays, shorter than 0.1 Å[3];
X (or Röntgen) rays, from 0.1 Å to 100 Å;
ultraviolet rays, from 100 Å to 4000 Å;
visible light rays, from 4000 Å to 8000 Å;
infrared rays, from 8000 Å to 240,000 Å;
and the electromagnetic (or radio) waves
    from about one-half millimeter to 30,000
    meters (about 18 miles).

[3] Å stands for Angstrom unit, which is equal to one ten-millionth of a millimeter.

But when a man happens to be in their path, he intercepts them and reacts by a burn, or serious injuries, to X-rays; by slight burns, ocular troubles, and pigmentation of the skin, to ultraviolet; by visual sensation and the sight of objects, to light waves; by the impression of heat, to infrared rays.

We have, therefore, on the one side, electromagnetic perturbations characterized by wave lengths or by periods expressed by numbers that can enter into mathematical formulas; and on the other side, the translations of these numbers into states of consciousness through the sensory system and man's brain cells: these are two aspects of the same events.

Now an extrapolation applies solely to a mathematical formula expressing an experimental law in which *only* wave lengths, or periods per second, intervene. Human intelligence, entirely exempt of sense contingencies, alone enters into play. But this extrapolation may deal with a range of radiations such that, *as we pass from one range of sensitivity to another,* other sense organs are brought into play. The experimental control of this extrapolation will not depend on the same sense organs, or the same cells. That is what I tried to express by saying that an extrapolation can conceivably transpose the objective phenomenon—number of periods per second—into a different qualitative plane. For instance, by passing from the visible red rays to the invisible infrared radiations, which no longer affect the consciousness of man through the same channels: the eye in the first case, the skin in the second. Even when we use a detecting instrument—a photoelectric tube, for instance—we may have to make a change: certain tubes are sensitive to visible ultraviolet rays but not to infrared.

PROBLEMS OF SCIENTIFIC INTERPRETATION

Argument

The goal of science is to foresee. As a consequence of the discontinuity of matter, our scientific laws are statistical laws; we explain them by the calculus of probabilities which admits a homogeneity based on chaos. On our "scale of observation" order is born of disorder.

These statistical laws enable us to foresee phenomena even though we do not understand how they work or their cause. We have to limit cause to the preceding event. However, when man intervenes it is generally simpler to consider his thought as the efficient cause. A personality appears able to influence events, but the statistical laws cannot take personality into account and a hypothesis is needed to bridge this gap.

Hypothesis is the soul of science. The more facts it covers the greater its value. It is useful even when it is false. Both knowledge and imagination are required to formulate a hypothesis. The two do not usually go together. Imagination flourishes most abundantly in youth. Education, together with the artificial life imposed by society, seems to smother it progressively.

3

PROBLEMS OF SCIENTIFIC INTERPRETATION

CERTAIN DIFFICULTIES · ORDER AND DISORDER · CAUS-
ALITY · HYPOTHESIS AND IMAGINATION

In the first chapter we stated that the goal of science is to foresee and that from this possibility of foreseeing we often gather the illusion that we understand. How can science foresee or, in other words, establish its laws?

Let us take an intelligent but completely ignorant man. (This is possible, though the opposite case is more frequent!) We will assume that this man is interested in certain questions dealing with humanity in general and that, moved by simple curiosity, he wants to know the proportion of girls and boys born every year. If he asks his immediate neighbors, say five or six families, he may possibly come to the conclusion that girls predominate. If he goes to some other place, he may meet another group that, on the contrary, will show a greater number of boys. If he restricts himself to one family, the difference, in one direction or the other, can be such that he will come to a conclusion in complete contradiction to what he thinks is true, though he is still unable to prove it; namely, that the number of boys and girls is about equal.

Our observer, by definition an intelligent man, will immediately infer that the number of cases he has dealt with is too small and he will pursue his investigations on a larger scale; a town, a state, a whole country or, better still, several countries. He will thus obtain the following results (the figures represent the ratio of the number of boys to that of girls):

France	1.047
Great Britain	1.063
Belgium	1.047
Denmark	1.050
Norway	1.056
Holland	1.047
Switzerland	1.052
Austria	1.061
Prussia	1.053
Finland	1.049
Spain	1.083
Greece	1.138
Italy	1.063
Portugal	1.071
Rumania	1.108

These figures give him a basis for comparison. He is therefore entitled to deduce the following law: in occidental countries, the number of masculine births is slightly higher (from 4 to 10 per cent) than that of feminine births. It is probable that a greater precision could be obtained if the experiment were prolonged for many years.

In this example, the accuracy increases with the number of cases. If the same observer had wanted to know the average height of the men of his country, he would have encountered other types of difficulties both at the start of the experiment and before being able to reach a conclusion. We must not forget that he is an intelligent man, and that he would immediately ask himself if origin, physiological defects, etc., should be taken into account. It seems absurd to decrease the "mean stature" of a group of men because there is a legless cripple amongst them or because a number of southerners who are of a slightly smaller build have settled in a northern country. He would naturally have to consider age. Thus, in spite of himself, the number of his observations would have to be limited to certain ethnical, or other well-defined groups, and his figures would not attain the character of generality he was looking for. Therefore, even in the simplest statistical calculation, it is necessary to have a relative homogeneity in the elements of the experiment. The most flagrant errors will result if this precaution is neglected. For instance, we often read in the newspapers that the duration of human life has been substantially increased since the 18th century, especially in the last fifty years. This is true, provided we use the expression "mean duration." However, the deduction that the duration of man's *individual* life has been increased is false. When the statistician states that life has been increased by twenty years, he does not claim that every man of sixty should live to be eighty, or that fifty or a hundred years ago, there were no octogenarians. His calculations are based, on the one hand, on the number of births, and on the other, on the "mean age" at which men die. To calculate the figure that represents the mean total duration of life he will add together *all* the ages at which *all* the individuals have died, including, of course, the ages of the children who have died in infancy, and he will divide this sum by the total number of births. We, therefore, have several ways of increasing the mean duration of life. Either by enabling a small number of men to live to be a hundred or by enabling a greater number to reach the age of sixty; or again, by diminishing infant mortality, and thus increasing the total sum of ages. The methods by which these different results can be obtained are identical: improvement in general hygiene, fighting against infectious diseases, etc. The results, which in a short time can be very important, do not signify, however, that the *individual* duration of human life has been increased. They mean that for every thousand children born, a *greater number* will reach the age of sixty. Naturally, if at the end of sixty years, a greater number are living, there is a greater chance that the number of octogenarians will be increased, and so on.

Two elements enter clearly into the calculation. One, which by protecting the individual and increasing his comfort, decreases the number of *external dangers* tending to interrupt his "normal" life; the other, which by allowing a greater number of individuals to escape the hazards of existence, first in childhood, and then at later ages, constantly increases the probabilities for a larger percentage to reach a very advanced age.

On the battlefield, when a handful of men rush forward under heavy fire, the number of those that arrive in the enemy trenches depends on the number that started. If twice as many start, it can be roughly admitted that double the number will attain the goal, provided that the intensity of fire has not varied in the interval. The fact that, out of a hundred newborn children, forty will, on an average, attain sixty years of age instead of twenty, as before Pasteur's time, not only increases the "mean duration" of human life, calculated as above, but assures a greater number of octogenarians and nonagenarians. And yet, the maximum individual duration of life has not varied in spite of the progress of hygiene and medicine. Life has not been prolonged, but old age has been brought within reach of a greater number of men. One can easily understand that the successes of medicine, which prolong life for many years, and prevent men from dying of certain diseases (insulin, for example, in the case of diabetes), help to increase the figure representing the mean duration of life. But it would occur to no one to say that they prolong the *normal* life of man. It is therefore evident that we must beware of the superficial interpretations of statistics. They can, it is true, give us data of extreme precision. We can even say that the only true precision obtainable is based on statistical calculations.

Everybody knows that fire or life insurance is based on this precision. We know by a long series of previous statistics how many houses will burn, or how many individuals will die in a certain country every year, excluding unforeseen cataclysms. This enables the companies to cover "ordinary" risks in return for a payment which is much less than the value of the house, for example, and yet make a profit. But though they can easily know how many fires will break out, and how many people will die, it is impossible for them to know which house will burn, or which one of their clients will die. The nature of the precision remains entirely impersonal and statistical. If there is an earthquake, a war, or an epidemic, the calculations are upset and the companies may fail. This corresponds to what we call "fluctuations." We shall discuss these later.

The most important consequence of the discontinuity of matter, of electricity, and of energy is that all our scientific laws are statistical laws whose precision depends on the immense number of elementary particles present. We cannot actually hope to attain a precision of another order, and, from a practical point of view, it would have no interest, as the precision attained statistically far exceeds the sensitivity of our instruments of observation. Moreover, certain problems can be treated as if matter were continuous. For instance, the propagation of heat by conductivity can be studied, from the point of view of continuity, by means of Fourier's differential equation or, from the point of view of discontinuity, on the basis of the kinetic theory of electronic conductivity. The two methods lead to the same results.

In a large number of cases we have no choice except to apply statistical methods. For example, in a cubic centimeter of gas at 0° and at atmospheric pressure, there are 3×10^{19} molecules.[1] In order to solve accurately any problem concerning this cubic centimeter, we would have to write down 3×10^{19} differential equations each containing 3×10^{19} terms representing the reciprocal actions of all these molecules two by two. Borel calculated that even if these molecules were only examined for one second each, it would be necessary to devote about twenty billion human lives to this work, whereas the kinetic theory, which considers statistically only the mean mass and the mean velocity (to be exact, half the product of the mass by the square of the velocity), enables us to solve easily a great number of problems concerning any volume of gas.

Our controls, namely, our instruments, are in many cases so coarse that even when we start from manifestly erroneous data, our results conform to the experiment. For instance, in the simplified demonstration of Boyle's law, based on the kinetic theory of gases, we assume that all the molecules have the same velocity—which is false; that all the shocks are central—which is false; and that the molecules can only move along paths parallel to the three axes

[1] 3 followed by 19 zeros.

of rectangular coordinates—which is false. Nevertheless, the result gives a correct expression of the law. However, when scientists try to obtain more accurate results and to increase the number of decimals, they find discrepancies that often lead to a discovery (in this particular case to the Van der Waals formula). As they were unable to apply the laws of rational mechanics to such complex phenomena and were faced by an immense number of elements, apparently devoid of personality, that is, *incapable of individually influencing the statistical law,* physicists had to resort to the calculus of probabilities. The mechanism of the laws of chance has been admirably analyzed by Professor Eugène Guye in his book, *L'Evolution Physico-Chimique,*[2] to which I refer the reader.

The kinetic theory of gases, which states that the pressure of a gas on the walls of a container is due to the impact of the molecules, is based on a fundamentally important postulate; namely, that the movements of the molecules are entirely governed by chance. In other words, we must admit that precise statistical laws are the result of absolutely disordered movements and complete chaos. This is evident, for it would be impossible to speak of the "pressure" inside of the vessel, if there were any order in these movements. If there were a privileged direction, certain parts of the wall inside the container would receive more shocks per unit of time, and would, therefore, be submitted to a higher pressure. The pressure of gas would not be a homogeneous phenomenon and could not be described statistically. To be able to apply the calculus of probabilities, we must accordingly assume this homogeneity based on

[2] Paris, Chiron, 1922. 2nd ed. revised and corrected, Hermann & Cie, 1939. English translation: *Physico-Chemical Evolution,* Methuen & Co., Ltd., London.

chaos. The individual laws that isolated molecules obey must, in consequence, disappear on our scale of observation, and all the individual movements must be summed up, in order that only the total phenomenon, which we call the pressure of gas, may persist.

The analysis of any phenomenon governed by one of our physico-chemical laws always brings us to the same conclusion: an absolute disorder at the base, which enables us, by means of the calculus of probabilities, to foresee the concatenation of the phenomena and their harmony. On our scale of observation order is born of disorder.

I remember that the first time I encountered this problem, while being initiated into the beauty of the kinetic theory of gases, I immediately thought of the magician who had delighted my young eyes by throwing a number of silk handkerchiefs pell-mell into a top hat, from which, after shooting off a pistol, he withdrew a live rabbit. I have since learned that the rabbit was hidden in the hat or in the table. But I have never understood the "trick" of the statistical laws. This may be due to my limited intelligence or because I give a different meaning to the word "understand" than do many of my colleagues. In reality, I grasp the mechanism of our reasoning, I do not question it, I have absolute confidence in it. But the fact that I can follow its different stages, step by step, does not give me the satisfaction that should logically follow complete comprehension. There is something I do not see: it is the link between the elementary chaos and the succession of phenomena that connect the former to the increasingly complex phenomena culminating in life.

It is evident that only statistical phenomena can be perceived directly—phenomena composed of an immense number of elementary facts. It is also evident that, as Poincaré said, the laws of chance do not signify an absence of laws, but laws so complex in their consequences that their detailed analysis completely escapes us and we can only grasp the general tendencies resulting from a large number of individual effects, which partially compensate each other. But when we start from a relatively simple phenomenon, and rise by degrees to a very complex one, I do not understand how the sole consideration of the laws of large numbers has enabled us to make up for our ignorance of the elementary laws, and to account quantitatively for the final phenomenon. It is true that these laws are only approximate and relative. Nevertheless, this is not wholly satisfactory, and an explanation that did not take consciousness into consideration would be more rational.

Let us take, for example, the displacement of a colloidal particle in a liquid. As a result of the shocks it receives from the molecules, its movements do not seem to obey any law (Brownian movement). It is a non-coordinated motion, "perfectly disordered," says Jean Perrin. It seems to be governed solely by the unknown whim of thermal agitation, and Carnot's law can only be applied to it with certain restrictions. But if, instead of considering one single particle, we observe a large number of similar particles in suspension, we see that the *mean* displacement of those particles is governed by Carnot's law and that the physicochemical laws of diffusion apply.

I stated above that the reason for my incomprehension might be due to the meaning I attribute to the word "understand." In the first chapter, we saw that a phenomenon is generally considered as "explained" when it has been broken up into a series of simpler phenomena, when an analogous mechanical model has been conceived, or when it can be foreseen mathematically from a few elementary facts that condition it. I apologize for coming back to this subject, but from my point of view this does not necessarily mean that one has understood it. We do not "understand" Planck's constant, nor the velocity limit of light, nor gravitation. Einstein's admirable hypothesis enables us to conceive a possible mechanism of universal attraction. But this is a human concept, for the use of our human brain, and nothing else. To know how to use data does not signify that we understand them, any more than to know how to drive a car, or pilot a plane, implies the comprehension or even the knowledge of all the mechanical details, and the chemical and electric laws that make them work. We do not understand the genesis of the universe, nor the evolution of organized beings, nor matter, nor energy, nor the quantum theory, nor the germination of a seed. This is entirely immaterial for the progress of science, which is only concerned with the "how" and never with the "why." Provided we can "foresee," the goal of science is fulfilled. But we must not lose sight of the relativity and superficial character of the answers furnished by science, when we wish to philosophize.

Our genius and our logic have enabled us to build a universe, full of hypothesis and mystery, from the elements furnished by the deforming mirror of our senses, but the relation between this image and the real universe remains, and will always remain, unknown to us. The splendor of the world springs from the impact between this colorless, silent universe and our consciousness, and we could paraphrase Rostand's beautiful verse and say: "O consciousness, without whose magic things would be but what they are !" [3]

We live on illusions. We have seen that when illusions

[3] "O Soleil, toi sans qui les choses ne seraient que ce qu'elles sont." Edmond Rostand, *Chantecler*.

are permanent, and universally shared, they constitute what we call reality and from that point of view science, which tends to unify these illusions, is real. We are only in danger of making grave errors when we tend, through pride, to confuse this reality, which is specifically human, with its cause, which will always escape us.

I have used the word "cause." Volumes have been written about it. Practically every philosopher or thinker has at some time or another been interested in the problem of causality. When examined from the simple angle of common sense, this notion is extremely complex for it is very difficult to define exactly what we mean by it. Every event has a cause and, more often, several causes. In the case of a cannon shot, for instance, shall we say that the firing of the shell is caused by the explosion of the percussion cap, or by the movement of the hand that pulled the string? Shall we say that the cause is the charge of powder? But without the movement of the hand, the charge could have remained inert for centuries. Nowadays all mechanical movements can be amplified and we may easily imagine that the explosion of the percussion cap, obtained by electrical means, was originally brought about by a feeble ray of light that could have been intercepted by the wing of a fly. We could have projected the ton of steel, which the shell weighs, thirty miles away by harnessing and amplifying a ray emitted by Sirius. The Chicago exposition in 1933 was lighted by a feeble ray, only a few photons, emitted by Arcturus forty years before. In the case of the cannon shot it would seem absurd to make the star responsible for the havoc wrought by the shell, and yet this slender beam of photons will have played as important a part in the firing of the shot as the charge of powder. Neither can we say that the workmen who manufactured the powder, nor the chemical engineers, nor the owners of the factory, nor the inventor of the formula, nor his mother, father, etc., are responsible. And yet, all of them, all the men who contributed to the construction of the cannon, share the responsibility, which gradually crumbles away *without ever disappearing completely* and reaches back to the origin of the world. And I have not even mentioned the psychological causes, without which there would have been neither shell, cannon, charge, percussion cap, nor the continuity of coordinated efforts with the object of making the shot go off.

We are, consequently, compelled to limit causality to precedence. Every phenomenon, act, or thought, which invariably precedes another phenomenon, can be considered as its cause. Experimentally, it is no more than an order of succession in time. But this again introduces certain difficulties. Conventionally speaking, the reaction that has immediately preceded a chemical reaction, and that always precedes it, cannot be called its "cause." In what we call "chain reactions," for example, the same succession of reactions is always produced in the same order. Instinctively, we neglect the successive causes, which often take place in a very short lapse of time, and consider the primary cause to be the chemist's mixing of the reacting bodies. We are once more faced with the same problem; if the mixture has to be heated to set off the reaction, the cause can just as well be the lighting of the Bunsen burner as the mixing of the products. Or else we can admit several causes that are inextricably linked, and then the unique cause may well be the will of the chemist to perform this experiment. We fall back on an imponderable, psychological cause.

Thus, when man intervenes, it is generally simpler to consider his thought as the efficient cause. But as this cause is in itself the result of one or several extraordinarily complex series of anterior causes, the word loses all significance. When we deal with longer intervals of time, this is still more striking. In the example of chain reactions given above, we said that they succeeded each other so rapidly that it was difficult to consider one of them as being the cause of the other, and that if we did, the word *cause* seemed to lose its usual significance. But if we study very slow reactions, such as those that took place during the geological periods, we may be tempted to consider an intermediary reaction as the cause of those that followed. In this case, we can no longer seek the primitive cause in a deliberate will, or we shall be severely criticized by the rationalists. However, as the cause that has been selected also has a cause, we are not much farther advanced.

I will briefly remind the reader of Kant's "Third Antinomy," as it is impossible to sum up the preceding thoughts more perfectly.

First the Thesis:

In going back from effect to cause, one should finally reach a cause that is not itself an effect; for, otherwise, one would never find *the whole cause*. Consequently, in the beginning there must have been an absolute cause.

And now the Antithesis:

An absolute first cause is inconceivable, inasmuch as it would not be linked by any law to its effect. There must then have been something that started the absolute cause at the determined moment.

We are thus faced with a rather embarrassing dilemma. How can we reconcile the purely statistical evolution of the universe in which, according to Boltzmann, each state tends toward a "more probable" state, with the individual impulses resulting from the psychological element: faith, love, hatred, ambition, greed, etc.?

We have just seen that when we try to determine the cause of a phenomenon or of an event, we necessarily arrive at badly defined beginnings, themselves the effect of an immense number of anterior causes, which, point by point, lead us back to the beginning of all things, to the origin of the world. We have seen that psychological causes, which seem to escape statistical laws, are as frequent as the material causes that obey them. On the other hand, we know that we cannot overlook man as the active element in an important series of phenomena constituting human evolution. This evolution can no more be denied than the evolution of radioactive substances. Furthermore, we know that, though we are *obliged* to consider the movements of the elementary particles that constitute the universe, as being entirely disordered, it is nevertheless not certain that this is the case. But only two possibilities exist: either there is order or there is disorder. If disorder prevails, then our statistical laws are comprehensible, but the notion of cause disappears, and the evolution of organized beings, and of man, becomes incomprehensible. If it is not completely disordered, then either privileged particles must exist that are entrusted with the coordination and obey laws that will always escape us, or there must be unknown coordinating forces, obeying a plan that we can only perceive by its macroscopic result. In this case there would be a first cause, and then one does not understand how pure statistical laws, which are based on chance alone, can explain the universe.

We have two hypotheses to choose from. In the first, the

elementary laws are unknowable, inaccessible to man's brain, not so much in themselves, individually, as because of the immense complexity of the elements present. In the second, what Pauli calls the "elementary inorganization" (*elementare Unordnung*) intervenes; every element is, or could be, identical to every other and is devoid of personality. Neither of these two hypotheses can explain evolution and its continuity, or the possibility of interpreting this evolution by means of purely statistical laws, without the help of a supplementary hypothesis.

The evolution of man must be connected in some way or another to the evolution of organized beings, and it seems difficult not to take into account man's intelligence, and his power of abstract thought, which is one of the most evident manifestations of this evolution. If it is nothing but an effect, this effect frequently plays the part of a cause; and at the present time, it can be stated that, for the past five or ten thousand years, this cause has become fundamental, not only as far as the evolution of man but also that of our earth is concerned. Who indeed can predict the remote consequences of the works that have been or will be undertaken by man? Who can affirm that evolution as a whole would have followed identically the same path, if man's intelligence had not created civilization?

We can never escape the following simple fact: everything takes place as if, under certain circumstances, the march of events could be influenced by a personality, through means that seem to escape the laws of large numbers and that cannot be detected by our instruments. On the other hand, the law of large numbers can never take individual personalities into account. There is a gap, as Borel points out: [4] "It seems to me that one of the most

---

[4] *Loc. cit.*, p. 297.

difficult things to explain in the theory of epiphenomenal consciousness is the fact that the simple play of a materialistic mechanism could have produced books in which abstract ideas and complicated sentiments are propounded; books which can considerably influence nature, through the intermediary of man. This miracle closely resembles the miracle of the 'typewriting monkeys,' but is even more improbable. The existence of this fact and its persistence through the ages strike me as being incomprehensible, unless one admits that man's abstract reason can have some influence on his line of thought and, consequently, on his acts."

This paragraph is very significant and important. It clearly expresses one of the gravest conflicts of modern science, and the personality of its author gives it special value.

At present there is less need for scientists and technicians than for distinguished minds with a highly scientific and mathematical culture who could get us out of the rut in which we are momentarily bogged. In short, we need men of science, capable of rising to the consideration of the fundamental problems of knowledge. They should be not only qualified to understand and to discuss the modern mathematical theories, but also to deal with general biological problems, or at least to recognize the phenomena and the difficulties raised by the study of living matter and organized beings. They must, evidently, also be familiar with the nervous system and its activities from a physical, chemical, and physiological point of view. In addition, they should possess a good philosophical culture and a profound knowledge of experimental psychology and of the physiology of sensations.

This program, obviously, already implies a rather restricted choice. If we add that they must, above all, be absolutely honest and endowed with intelligence and brilliant imagination, we must admit that, even without being pessimistic, an immediate solution of this conflict cannot be expected. All the more so as two of the requisites are in a certain measure contradictory: namely, the accumulation of knowledge and the possession of imagination. Indeed it seems probable that imagination, the source of hypothesis, is much richer and more active when the mind is fresh and young. But it would take many long years of work to accumulate sufficient science and the delicate flower of imagination would gradually be stifled. Such a man, after he had finally mastered the necessary foundations with which to face nature and to try and understand it, would be incapable of formulating the daring hypotheses, which might eventually lead to the solution. *The man of science who cannot formulate a hypothesis is only an accountant of phenomena.*

Hypothesis is the stamp imprinted by the human mind on the simple succession of facts. Through the intermediary of our senses, extended by our instruments, nature furnishes rough phenomena which follow each other in time. Our intelligence grasps this enumeration and tries to create a plausible fairy story in which each event plays an indispensable part in the birth of subsequent events and is a consequence of past events. This fairy story is the hypothesis, the fundamental tool of scientific work. It rests entirely on one of the most extraordinary qualities of the human mind, imagination—science would not exist without it. It is not a method, for it cannot be transmitted. It is the result of an individual gift, which cannot be specifically differentiated from literary or philosophical genius. The more facts it covers, the greater its value, but it is never useless, even when it is false. Indeed when a hypothesis is formulated in order to explain the concatenation of a series of phenomena, the scientist establishes a program of work and plans experiments to prove or disprove his preconceived idea. The nature of the answer is immaterial. If the hypothesis is confirmed, the research program continues logically, until a difficulty arises. If it is disproved, it usually leads to a modification of the hypothesis, which makes it possible for the new fact to be incorporated. Sometimes the whole hypothesis must be changed. Such is the fate of science.

A hypothesis is still useful when, though false, it is nevertheless backed by a certain number of scientists who have helped to construct it, and who are sentimentally, one might say paternally, attached to it. Their conviction is based on experiments that lack precision or that can give rise to different interpretations. As a rule, one individual worker, or a group of workers, remains unconvinced, but can only express his opinion in print, provided it is substantiated by facts. Hence the necessity of combining and executing a series of experiments in the laboratory. A wrong hypothesis, therefore, will sometimes give rise to more experiments than a true one and will contribute as much to the progress of knowledge.

The world should be grateful to scientists endowed with imagination who bring out a new hypothesis, no matter how improbable it may seem. As a matter of fact, the most important have been the most daring, and the most violently attacked at the start. One need only recall how the scientific world greeted the announcement by Svante Arrhenius, who was only twenty-four years old, that molecules in solution were dissociated into "ions." He created a real revolution. and the indignation was as high as when

Pasteur announced that infectious diseases were caused by "microbes."

With a few outstanding exceptions, every great stride in science has been greeted with disbelief and an almost unanimous revolt of the scientific world. This in no way implies that every revolutionary theory constitutes a step forward. Far from it, but it signifies that official bodies have a tendency to be hasty in their judgments and to obey certain non-scientific considerations when tradition is menaced.

Imagination, bolstered by facts, is the mother of hypothesis, and hypothesis is the soul of science. It would, therefore, be useful to develop imagination. This, however, appears impossible. Imagination is a gift that characterizes youth and seems to be about equally distributed amongst children who belong to any one ethnical group. It is undoubtedly stronger between the ages of five and ten, and education appears to smother it progressively.

The imagination of a child who plays with his doll, his horse, or his railroad is unsurpassed. They are not playthings for him, but the pretext to live an active existence, as real as his family life, often more intense, and peopled by beings more alive than those who actually surround him. Education gradually fills his brain with outside facts, which must become the elements of the artificial life imposed by society. Moving pictures help to stifle his personality by distracting his attention, and by deluding him on his aptitudes, his tastes, and life in general.

Obviously, all children do not have the same quality of imagination. The quality depends to a certain extent on the intelligence, which is very unequally distributed. The percentage of highly intelligent children is slight, as is the percentage of children who will one day be able to jump 6 feet 5 inches or to run the 100-yard dash in 10 seconds flat. The number of men who are gifted with real creative imagination is very limited and this imagination rarely persists beyond the thirty-fifth year. It generally bears its most brilliant fruit between the ages of twenty and thirty. The best proof of this is the age of Nobel prize winners, or rather their age when they made the discovery that won them the prize. I will name only a few of the most famous and recent ones, who were less than thirty-five years old: Arrhenius, Einstein, Bohr, Millikan, Compton, Carrel, Banting, Debye, Heisenberg, Fermi, Louis de Broglie, Joliot, Svedberg, Siegbahn, Raman, Dirac, Anderson, Bragg, etc. Two of the greatest mathematicians, Abel and Evariste Galois, who lived before the Nobel prize existed, died before their twenty-fifth year.[5]

It could be argued that a number of prominent scientists accomplished their best work when they were past forty and continued working until they were well over seventy or eighty. That is true; but either they were exceptions, which always exist (Pasteur, Berthelot, Loeb, Claude Bernard, Landsteiner, Lorentz, Millikan, etc.) or else the original thought, the true creative spark that oriented all their future work, can be traced back to the period that elapsed between the twentieth and thirty-fifth year. This origin is not always easy to find and the connection of ideas is not always clear, but it can often be established. In the case of Pasteur, for instance, it is easy to link up his whole life's work to his general ideas on the dissymmetry of the universe. These ideas were based on his first experiments with sodium tartrate and paratartrate. The starting point was before his thirtieth year, and his whole life was not long enough to exploit this brilliant idea, which was so

---

[5] *Viz.* Auguste Comte: "What is the life of a great man? It is a thought of youth realized in maturity." See also: W. Oswald: *Great Men.*

fertile that it spread to a number of other sciences; eighty years later, the mine is not yet exhausted.

The scientist with imagination is the pioneer of progress. His hypotheses reveal new fields unsuspected by the crowd of workers who gradually take possession of them as official science becomes reconciled. Science would not evolve, or would progress extremely slowly, if ten or twelve men of genius did not exist per century. Ten or twelve individuals, out of the two billion that constitute the population of the globe, represent but 0.000,000,5 per cent, and for one generation this percentage should be divided by 4, if we admit that there are about four generations per century.

FURTHER PROBLEMS OF SCIENTIFIC
INTERPRETATION

Argument

Although we can conceive a phenomenon which is
ideally reversible, most phenomena including those pertaining to life are irreversible. This irreversibility can be
explained by the calculus of probabilities and linked to the
Second Law of Thermodynamics.

The derogations which occur in the calculus of probabilities are called fluctuations. When the number of particles involved is large, the fluctuations are so slight in comparison that they cannot be detected by our instruments.
When the number of particles is small, the fluctuations can
become the principal factor, with the result that the statistical laws no longer apply. This is the case in certain small
elements of the cell where fluctuations are able to play a
preponderant role. It is possible that these elements may
escape the law of chance and thus play a fundamental part
in the evolution of living beings.

Entropy increases as energy decreases and therefore expresses the trend of the universe toward disorder. It is the
signpost for time in the physical world.

The laws of wave mechanics demonstrate our atomic
concept but they are reversible in relation to time. Can we
reconcile the reversibility of wave mechanics with the irreversibility of thermodynamics?

4

FURTHER PROBLEMS OF SCIENTIFIC INTERPRETATION

CALCULUS OF PROBABILITIES · IRREVERSIBILITY · THE
SECOND PRINCIPLE OF THERMODYNAMICS

THE human mind wants to understand, and it can only understand by simplifying. Simplification, however, is always arbitrary and tends to separate us from reality. Therefore, when man tries to understand he always diverges from the problem he meant to study. *A sensation, atomistically conceived, has no meaning.* The need to unify and to discover the elements that are common to all phenomena leads man, in spite of himself, into other fields than those he meant to explore. In this search for unity, he sometimes succeeds in formulating general laws, principles, which show an impressive character of generality and great breadth, at least when applied to unorganized matter.

In the preceding pages we spoke of the law of large numbers and of the calculus of probabilities, both of which are in fact the foundation of our physical and chemical laws. It may be useful to remind the layman of the reasonings and elementary calculations on which these laws are based and from which the mathematical expression of abstract concepts, such as entropy, emerge.

*   *   *

I will not dwell on the discontinuous structure of matter, which is a familiar notion to everybody nowadays, and will only remind the reader that the first step on the road to discontinuity was taken by the chemists. The existence of atoms and molecules was denied for many years, but is now universally admitted. The fundamental laws of definite or multiple proportions, which are at the base of the atomic theory, would be difficult to explain in any other way, and it would be impossible to account for the phenomena of adsorption and molecular organization at the surface of liquids and solids.

This discontinuity is found everywhere in the realm of physics and, particularly, in the kinetic theories, which Daniel Bernoulli was the first to establish scientifically. The most important constants of the kinetic theory of gases were confirmed with a fairly close approximation by Perrin's experiments on the Brownian movement.

We know that this discontinuity of matter has been extended to the realm of electricity (positive and negative electrons) and to that of energy by the fruitful hypothesis of quanta.

We have already seen that one of the most important consequences of this granular structure of the universe is the great number of elements that enter into play in the smallest phenomenon, and in the slightest experiment. We have also shown the insurmountable difficulties that would arise if we tried to calculate the simplest phenomenon in an exhaustive way. The task would be difficult, even if we could dispose of all the necessary elements for the calculation, which is not certain.

The calculus of probabilities has the inestimable advantage of enabling us to pursue our investigations in a realm where the methods of rational mechanics would be utterly powerless. This advantage is not without drawbacks, for in no section of mathematics is it so easy to make a false start. However, there is a compensation to these false starts, which is quite instructive. On page 66 we mentioned the possibility of reaching a correct result when starting from false data and this suffices to convince us of the coarseness of our experimental methods and scientific instruments. We often resemble an aviator who would attempt to study the life of insects on earth from an altitude of 30,000 feet.

The probability of an event is defined in the following manner: It is the ratio of the number of cases favorable to the event, to the total number of possible cases, *all possible cases being considered as equally probable.*

For instance, in the simplest case of all, in a game of heads or tails, the number of possible cases is evidently 2 (heads and tails). If, as is usual, the coin is symmetrical, the two cases are equally probable; therefore, the probability for obtaining heads (or tails), when tossing the coin in the air, is equal to 1 divided by 2, or ½ or 0.5.

We must also remember that, as Joseph Bertrand cleverly remarked, "chance has neither consciousness nor memory." At the end of 10 throws, which have brought up heads, the chance that the next throw will again bring up heads is the same as after the first throw, and the same as for tails; the probability is still 0.5.

The principle of evolution of physico-chemical phenomena. Reversible and irreversible phenomena.[1]

A phenomenon is only reversible when it is possible to reproduce all its phases successively and in an inverse direction. It is easy to *conceive* a perfectly reversible phenomenon: for example in mechanics, the oscillation of a pendulum; in physico-chemistry, the growth of a crystal of ice when water is cooled or its fusion when water is heated. It is difficult, however, to *attain this ideal reversibility in actual practice.* In the case of the pendulum or any other mechanical model, we find that we can never eliminate friction, which is a source of heat. In the case of the crystal, the ideal condition of irreversibility can never be attained in conformity with classical thermodynamics, which specifies that a system is ideally reversible when every one of the successive states through which it passes differs only infinitesimally from a state of equilibrium.

In reality, phenomena that appear to be ideally reversible are only imperfectly so. There is an important category of phenomena that seems to escape all reversibility. For example, the fall of a body by the action of gravitation. We know that the kinetic energy acquired through the fall is transformed into heat, which is dissipated into the surrounding medium. We also know that, if we furnish this body with a quantity of heat energy exactly equal to that which was developed by the arrest of its fall, it will not rise to its initial level. This is a clear case of absolute irreversibility.

Let us now consider two different gases at the same temperature, enclosed in two vessels communicating with

[1] In this chapter we borrow the order, examples, and sometimes the text of Guye, in his admirable book *L'Evolution Physico-Chimique.* We are convinced that this subject cannot be more clearly explained.

each other by a stopcock. If the latter is open (Berthollet's experiment), the two gases, after a certain length of time, are homogeneously mixed through diffusion, and the most accurate analysis does not show the slightest difference in the composition of the mixture. If the gases in question are "perfect gases," incapable of reacting chemically on each other, this chemical mixture will not have given rise to either liberation or absorption of heat: the energy of the mixture will be equal to the energy that the two gases would have had separately. It is evident that no matter how long we wait in the hope of witnessing the reverse phenomenon, we shall be disappointed; the mixture will remain as homogeneous as possible. This phenomenon therefore is apparently ideally irreversible.

Finally, if we turn to the more complex phenomena of life, we will perceive that they have an indisputable character of irreversibility. We have never seen a living being evolve in a direction that was inverse to the normal. A dead man does not resuscitate and rejuvenate, no matter what the conditions are, whereas water can be transformed into steam, and then condensed into a liquid form, if the necessary conditions are fulfilled.

Thus irreversible phenomena exist, or to be more exact, phenomena whose reversibility has never been observed.

Irreversibility has been correlated with *probability,* and this is of the greatest importance. Everybody knows that if a black and a white powder are shaken together an almost uniform mixture will finally be obtained, which gives the impression of being a gray powder. When this result has been reached, experience teaches us that we can go on shaking the mixture indefinitely, without changing the appearance of the gray powder. *On our scale of observation,* the phenomenon is not further modified although the grains constituting the mixture occupy different positions every time we shake them. The mixture of the two powders, therefore, constitutes (on our scale of observation) an irreversible phenomenon, and we will try to understand its mechanism.

Let us imagine that we have a powder composed of only 10 white grains and 10 black ones differing from each other only by their superficial coloring. At the beginning of the experiment these grains are placed in a glass tube the diameter of which is only slightly larger than that of the grains themselves, so that they will all be superposed in a single column. The 10 black grains occupy the lower part of the tube, and the 10 white ones the upper. On our scale of observation, the tube in this initial stage is half black and half white.

This tube is closed at one end and communicates at the other with a hollow glass ball. When we turn it upside down the grains fall, pell-mell, into the ball, and when we turn it up again, they fall back into the tube. If we shake the tube while making this experiment the grains will fall into different positions and it is most improbable that the black grains will all be together as they were at the beginning. At a proper distance, far enough for the eye to be unable to distinguish the black grains from the white ones, the whole length of the tube will appear gray.

Let us then shake and turn them up once more. The grains will be arranged differently but, on our scale of observation, the tube remains gray. The phenomenon is not modified, and observation teaches us that it persists, even when we prolong the experiment for a great length of time.

The calculus of probabilities will now enable us to give an exact statement of the facts.

Following Guye, let us evaluate the total number of permutations that can be made with only 20 grains, that is, the number of different arrangements that can be obtained. Combinatorial analysis gives the simple formula that applies to this problem. We find for the number of permutations:

$$P_{20} = 20! = 2,432,902,008,176,640,000$$

(the symbol: 20! is read: factorial 20), or approximately: $P_{20} = 243,290 \times 10^{13}$.

Thus we can arrange the 20 grains in our tube in more than two billion billion different ways.

But it is impossible for us to discern the individual grains at a distance and, therefore, among all the permutations that we can imagine, there are a considerable number that produce the same impression on our eye and that, on our scale of observation, we call the same phenomenon.

Our mathematical problem is now somewhat different. We have 20 grains, of which 10 are white and 10 are black. In the following table (also from Guye) we see how many permutations correspond to each arrangement of the grains in respect to color.

This table shows us, in the first place, that among all the possible permutations, there are about 10^{13} (more than 10 thousand billions) which will separate the 10 black grains from the 10 white ones. This is the number of permutations that are capable of bringing back the initial stage, namely the separation of the black and white powders. Although this number is very great in absolute value, it is nevertheless incomparably small compared to the total number of permutations, P_{20}. It is even very small as compared to the number of permutations that lead to five white and five black grains being in each half of the tube. (63,504 times smaller).

Number of black and white grains in one of the halves of the tube				Corresponding number of permutations	Probability of the appearance of one class of permutations
10	white	0	black	$1 \times A$	0.0000 054
9	"	1	"	$100 \times A$	0.0005 4··
8	"	2	"	$2025 \times A$	0.0109 7··
7	"	3	"	$14400 \times A$	0.0780 ...
6	"	4	"	$44100 \times A$	0.2388 ...
5	"	5	"	$63504 \times A$	0.3439 ...
4	"	6	"	$44100 \times A$	0.2388 ...
3	"	7	"	$14400 \times A$	0.0780 ...
2	"	8	"	$2025 \times A$	0.0109 7··
1	"	9	"	$100 \times A$	0.0005 4··
0	"	10	"	$1 \times A$	0.0000 054
				$\overline{184,756 \times A}$	1.0000

$$A = 10! \ 10! = 13,168,189,400,000 = 1.3 \times 10^{13}$$

It is obvious that this last class of permutations is the one that gives the same medium color to the upper part of the tube as to the lower. It constitutes the most numerous class of permutations and consequently corresponds to the most probable phenomenon.

Thus, according to the table, it would be necessary to shake the tube 184,756 times "on the average" in order to have one chance of getting back to *an equivalent initial state,* that is, a state producing the same impression on our eyes. If we only shake the tube once, the probability that this agitation will bring about this initial state (the most heterogeneous), is therefore $\dfrac{1}{184,756}$ and we will say that the probability that the phenomenon is reversible, on our scale of observation, is $\dfrac{1}{184,756}$. The probability that the distribution of grains will be five black and five white at the top and at the bottom, that is to say, the most homogeneous arrangement, is, as we have seen, 63,504 times greater.

We thus understand why the phenomenon only evolves in one direction, and why it is irreversible. If the separation of a gray powder into its two constituent parts by agitation does not take place, it is not because this is impossible, but because this is only *very improbable*. The same reasoning holds true when the number of grains, or molecules, is very great, as in the example of the two gases cited above. Whenever the elements become fairly numerous, the probability of a return to the original separation (complete heterogeneity) becomes so small that we do not hesitate to say that the phenomenon is impossible, though in reality it is only very improbable.

To give an idea of this, let us again take up some of Guye's calculations.[2] If, instead of 10 white grains and 10 black ones, we have 100, the probability of the appearance of the class of permutations corresponding to a uniform mixture of the 50 white and 50 black grains decreases from 0.3439 (in the case of the 10 grains of each color) to 0.110. But the probability that the 50 black grains will be together, and separated from the white, which in the previous case (20 grains in all) was 0.000,0054 decreases all the way to 1.105×10^{-59}, or a decimal number with 58 zeros (instead of 5) to the right of the point. If we consider 1000 particles instead of 10, this last probability is expressed by

[2] *Les Frontières de la Physique et de la Biologie,* Hermann & Cie. Paris, 2nd ed.

0.489 $\times$ 10^{-600}, or 489 preceded by 599 zeros to the right of the point. On the contrary, the probability of the appearance of a homogeneous gray mixture has only become 10 times less.

A close scrutiny of the table published by Guye in the book we have quoted led him to the following interesting observation: when the number of grains increases, we have a rather abrupt passage from uniform distribution (homogeneous gray mixture) to non-uniform distribution (heterogeneity, white separated from black), that is, from statistical properties to individual properties.

Now if we consider that in a cubic millimeter of gas at 0°C. and at a pressure of 760 mm. there are 3 $\times$ 10^{16} molecules (or 30 million billion) we realize the order of magnitude of the probability for a mixture of two half cubic millimeters of gas to separate spontaneously. These simple examples will make it clear why the word "impossible" is never used in statistical physics, why it has been replaced by the terms: "highly improbable," or "very slightly probable," and how the two are practically equivalent.

The preceding observations show in a tangible manner that a phenomenon (black, white, or gray powder) can be considered as the expression of the laws of probabilities on our scale of observation.

In short, the example of the powders lays emphasis on the crucial point so strikingly expressed by Guye: *It is essentially the scale of observation that creates the phenomenon.* This sentence clarifies what was said at the beginning of this book, for as Guye himself wrote: "Closely connected with the mystery of these laws of infinitely complex effects is the no smaller mystery of the thinking being, without which neither scale of observation nor, consequently, the phenomenon, could exist."

We thus see how easily and inevitably a simple analysis of the actual method of studying physico-chemical problems leads straight to philosophic considerations.

The reversibility of the phenomenon of the diffusion of gases, considered as highly improbable but not rigorously impossible, is easily understood. Let us now consider the contrast between uniformly-distributed motions, such as constitute heat, and the motion of a falling or rising body.

During the fall of a body submitted to gravitational attraction, its molecules, independently of their movements of thermal agitation, have acquired a downward velocity. This velocity is the cause of what is called in mechanics the "kinetic energy" of the falling body. Then when the body strikes the earth, this directed kinetic energy is transformed by the unknown play of molecular actions (equivalent, by its complexity, to a kind of agitation) into an uncoordinated motion. This corresponds to the uniform distribution of which we earlier spoke. As this movement is added to the thermal agitation, the temperature of the body has risen.

Then if we heat a body with the chimerical hope of causing it to re-ascend to its original level, we again endow it with uncoordinated motion. This motion is incapable, by the very fact of its uniform distribution, of giving rise to an appreciable motion of the whole in any direction whatever, much less of raising the body to its initial level. To obtain such a result, it would be necessary that, by a singular coincidence and at a given instant, all the molecules constituting the body should have equal velocities in the same direction.

At this point the fundamental question arises: Can such a singular distribution of velocities be produced by thermal agitation alone? In answer to this question the opponents of the new concepts, who, it must be admitted, are less and less numerous, will be ready to assert definitely that it is absolutely impossible for thermal agitation to produce such a distribution. Nobody can contradict them.

On the other hand, the partisans of the new concepts, without knowing more about the mechanism of thermal agitation than the others, will declare equally definitely that thermal agitation, by its very complexity, can bring about any kind of distribution, even that in which all velocities are parallel, so long as the total energy remains constant. Evidently, such distributions are incomparably less numerous than the uniform ones, which leave the body as a whole motionless. The supporters of this point of view will say: The proof that this concept is likely lies in the fact that thermal agitation is quite capable of throwing very small particles upwards (Brownian movement). It is, therefore, a question of degree, but the phenomenon is possible. And they will repeat with Herodotus and Amiel: "Let time be lavished, and everything possible happens." A little farther on we shall see the weak point of this argument.

At present this seems to be the point of view that dominates the thoughts of physicists concerning irreversibility.

The second principle of thermodynamics, considered as a principle of evolution.

Following Guye, let us now consider how the concept of irreversibility is linked to the second principle of thermodynamics. The definitions that have been given of the second principle are very often incomplete; in fact it is difficult to define it in a general and rigorous way, and at the same time evoke the underlying idea. This principle is, therefore, often defined by one or other of its consequences (see Planck's *Thermodynamics*).

Examples: (a) heat cannot of itself pass from a colder to a hotter body, unless a correlative modification is produced somewhere; (b) it is impossible to conceive a thermal machine continuously transforming heat into mechanical work, without having at least two sources at different temperatures; (c) the quantity of energy that can be transformed into mechanical work is continuously decreasing—energy degrades itself and the universe tends toward immobility, etc.

Clausius was the first to give a satisfactory definition of Carnot's principle, by introducing the concept of entropy. The second principle of thermodynamics thus became the principle of the increase of entropy (Carnot-Clausius).

We shall not review all the considerations that led to the definition of entropy but shall simply recall a few important points.

Let us consider an *isolated system* which can be as large as we please; our visible universe for example. Every state through which this system passes has a function the value of which depends only on the actual state of the system. Clausius has called this function *entropy* and it is designated by the symbol S.

We do not know the absolute value of the entropy of a body, any more than we know the absolute value of its energy or of its velocity. The only quantities we can determine experimentally are the variations of entropy, of energy, of velocity, etc. Furthermore, when a system is in equilibrium, its entropy is maximum; this involves the conditions $dS = 0$.

But the special characteristic of entropy is that it can

only increase when physico-chemical phenomena occur in the interior of the system. This one-way progression, *always in the direction of an irreversible degradation,* is the reason why the second principle of thermodynamics has been called a *principle of evolution.*

The point we now want to emphasize is the way in which the idea of irreversibility is connected with the second principle.

Clausius demonstrated that, when an isolated system passes from one state to another, entropy can only increase if irreversible phenomena take place in the interior of the system. The increase of entropy thus becomes a measure of irreversibility. If all the phenomena taking place in the interior of the system were ideally reversible, entropy would remain constant. But we have seen that this extreme case is never realized. In practice there is something irreversible in all physico-chemical transformations, so that in reality the entropy of a system will not remain constant, but will continually increase.[3] This was approximately the state of the problem when Gibbs and Boltzmann published their findings.

Boltzmann had the great merit of showing that the entropy S of an isolated system was connected with the probability p of its actual state by the relation

$$S = K \log_e p + C.$$

C being an undetermined constant.

[3] The preceding statements show the considerable importance of the Carnot-Clausius principle. We shall see later on that this is not its only interest, and that by the mere fact that it expresses an asymmetrical proposition with respect to the two directions of the current of time (past and future), it is the only theorem that can determine the unidirectional character of physical time. It can be considered as the one way of measuring physical time that is not periodical or, at any rate, that has a period so great that it exceeds the limits of the duration of the universe.

In other words, the variable part of the entropy of a system is proportional to the logarithm of the probability p of its present state. It immediately follows that the change of entropy, between two successive states, is proportional to the difference between the logarithms of the probabilities of these two states; therefore:

$$S_2 - S_1 = K \ (\text{Log } p_2 - \text{Log } p_1) = K \ \text{Log } \frac{p_2}{p_1}$$

As $S_2 - S_1$ is always positive, since the entropy of an isolated system can only increase, it follows that p_2 is greater than p_1, i.e., that the second state is *more probable* than the first.

When we say that, in passing from the first state to the second state, entropy increases, *we therefore assert that the system has evolved toward a more probable state.* If the system continues its evolution, under the action of the physico-chemical phenomena that occur in its interior, it will end by attaining a state of equilibrium. Thermodynamics shows that entropy is maximum at that moment. The same, therefore, will be true of the probability that corresponds to the state of equilibrium. This is indeed what we observed in the mixture of black and white grains. The equilibrium attained by the agitation corresponds to the most probable class of permutations, those that result in a uniform gray mixture in the two halves of the tube.

It is this approximately uniform mixture that can be called *the position of equilibrium of the system under the action of agitation.*

Fluctuations

The calculus of probabilities applied to physical and chemical phenomena can never furnish an absolute quantitative answer. For instance, in the example of the black and white powders we see that the mixture gives a gray powder, and that this can be predicted by calculation. But if, instead of dealing with what can logically be called a powder, namely an immense number of particles (100 grams of meal and 100 grams of finely pulverized charcoal), we should deal with 10 white and 10 black particles, we observe that the gray is not always the same. In the upper part of the tube, which was occupied by the 10 white particles, for example, we can have 5 of each color, disposed differently: 3 continuous white particles, 3 black, 2 white, 2 black; or again, 4 white particles, 1 black, 1 white, and 4 black. It is evident that a great number of more or less probable combinations are possible, and that certain of these will determine a very different impression on our retina from the one we would have if every white particle was next to a black one.

The macroscopic phenomenon "gray" is therefore not very well defined and corresponds to an approximate equilibrium which, when analyzed with a small number of units, as we have just done, is far from constant. The deviations in either direction from the most probable distribution are called *fluctuations*.

These fluctuations—which we already observed when trying to compare the number of male and female births —obviously become more important as the number of units entering into play become smaller. With 10 black and 10 white grains they are evident. The composition of the mixture, which fills each half of the tube, will oscillate around the most probable value corresponding to the theoretical equilibrium.

In ten games of heads or tails, one of the players has an excellent chance of winning. In a pound of meal, or even a gram mixed with a gram of charcoal, the differences will be absolutely imperceptible. In a million games of heads or tails, the ratio of the number of games won by each player to the total number of games will be almost identical. In the case of the powders, or in any other analogous case, the importance of the fluctuations decreases as the number increases; the influence of the "mean fluctuation" [4] becomes smaller and smaller, and ends by being negligible.

We can now understand the meaning of the expression "law of large numbers," or "statistical laws." Their precision depends on the number of particles or molecules present, or on the number of events considered.

It is easy to obtain an idea of the precision attained by taking another example: that of two communicating vessels containing a gas. If the two vessels have a total capacity of only 1 cubic centimeter ($\frac{1}{2}$ cc. each), they contain at $0°$C., and at the barometric pressure of 760 mm., 3×10^{19} molecules, or 30 billion billion molecules. We know that the molecules constantly pass from one vessel to another as a consequence of the thermal agitation. But as the pressure is due to the shocks against the walls, there is a difference of pressure in the two vessels as soon as the number is not identically the same in each. The pressure is proportional to the number of molecules per cubic centimeter, to their mass, and to their velocity. If, therefore, we admit that at a given moment one of the vessels contains 1 million more molecules than the other— which represents a considerable, and rather improbable, deviation—the difference in pressure would be less than one ten-billionth of 1 per cent, or less than one ten thou-

[4] We refer the reader to Guye's book for the exact definition and the mathematical expression of the term "mean fluctuations." P. 52 (1st ed.).

sandth of one thousandth of a millimeter of mercury. This difference is much too small to be measured by our most sensitive instruments. We can, therefore, observe no difference and even if there were 100 million more molecules on one side than on the other, we would be unable to perceive it.

If the volume of the vessels were reduced from one cubic centimeter to one cubic micron,* that is, if it were one thousand billion times less, they would still contain about 30 million molecules of gas. The same difference of one million between them would then result in a difference in pressure of about 7 per cent. But if we still further mentally decrease this volume to a point where the two vessels will only contain 10 molecules each, then the passage of one molecule from one vessel to another will determine a difference in pressure of the order of 20 per cent (9 on one side, 11 on the other).

Thus, when the number of particles or units that enter into play is considerable, the fluctuations, even if slightly probable, even if important in absolute value, only introduce in the macroscopic phenomenon, on our scale of observation, variations of an order of magnitude greatly inferior to that which can be revealed by our most refined methods of measurement. Our "statistical" laws can then attain a degree of precision that is far superior to our methods of control: but they always remain approximate, and they are only valid on our scale of observation.

On the contrary, when the number of units in the experiment is small, even the most probable and, there-

* EDITOR'S NOTE: A cubic centimeter is the volume of a cube, each edge of which measures 0.3937 inch. A cubic micron is the volume of a cube, each edge of which measures 39.37 millionths of an inch.

fore, the most frequent fluctuations introduce variations such that the statistical law is no longer valid. In the case of the small communicating vessels, for example, we can no longer state that the pressure is equal: *This equality of pressure occurs only exceptionally.* In this case the laws of the individual actions of molecules, which are unknown to us, enter into play and fluctuation becomes the principal factor.

We have chosen an extreme example, but it is not an improbable one, if we consider the cellular elements of living organisms. The volume of cells varies from around 10 to 100 cubic microns. Certain elements, visible in the microscope or in the ultra-microscope, are still smaller. We are ignorant of the part played by most of them, but Thomas Hunt Morgan has clearly established the role of the genes (units composing the chromosomes) in heredity. Therefore, it is not absurd to think that extremely small units, of the order of one thousandth or one ten thousandth of a cubic micron, play a fundamental part in the evolution of living beings.

Now the protein molecules, which these units contain and which constitute them, are much larger than the molecules of a gas, whose mean diameter is of the order of 1 Ångström, which is equal to one two hundred and fifty millionth of an inch. The molecular weight of a typical protein, egg-albumin, is about 35,000 and its length is approximately 40 Ångströms. We know of some proteins that have a molecular weight of the order of one million (blood pigments of invertebrates). The molecular weight of serum albumin is roughly 69,000 and of serum globulins 136,000. The volume of these molecules lies between about 40,000 and 200,000 cubic Ångströms. One cubic micron would contain about 30 million molecules of egg albumin.

In a volume of 0.1 cubic micron there would be 30,000 and a volume of 0.01 cubic micron would only contain 30. These figures must be further divided by 10, if we consider a solution at a concentration equivalent to that of serum.

These are clearly approximate figures and they can only give a rough order of magnitude. Nevertheless, they show that as soon as we deal with volumes of the order of 1/10 of a cubic micron—certain cellular elements endowed with important biological properties are probably even smaller—*we reach a domain where the laws of large numbers can no longer apply rigorously, and where the role of fluctuations becomes preponderant.*

Chance is at the base of the calculus of probabilities and of all our physical and chemical laws, and it enables us to attain a very great precision because of the immense number of elements. But when we deal with fluctuations, this is not the case. We can calculate the chances for a certain fluctuation to appear in preference to another less probable one. However, when we have such a small number of units the fluctuations, to one side or another of the most probable distribution, are continuous and any precise prediction becomes impossible. We recall that the statistics for all the European countries enable us to predict the ratio of the number of male births to that of female births within about 2 or 3 per cent. This precision would be very much increased, if the experiment had been carried on for a greater number of years. But, at the other extreme, if we had limited our statistics to 2 or 3 families, we might have made an error of as much as 50 per cent.

* * *

The second principle of thermodynamics, which enables us to interpret the evolution of our physico-chemical universe with great precision, can in the case of living organisms be subjected to important and fundamental restrictions.

We learn through thermodynamics that entropy reaches a maximum at the moment of equilibrium. Fluctuations are not taken into account, for we assume—generally rightly so—that they are practically negligible, namely *incapable of modifying the phenomenon on our scale of observation.* But as a result of fluctuations a system is constantly oscillating around its theoretical equilibrium. It follows that entropy, which is always proportional to the logarithm of the probability of an event, will be more or less diverted from its theoretical value by the oscillations to which it is subjected. A series of fluctuations in a given direction—which is always possible—or one rare but very important fluctuation can, therefore, decrease entropy by quantities that are no longer impossible to measure, and that make it frankly evolve in the opposite direction.

Entropy is one of the most admirable concepts created by the human mind. The men who successively conceived, modeled, perfected, and generalized it—Carnot, Clausius, Gibbs, Boltzmann—died without realizing how important this child of their genius had become with age, and how many philosophical problems it raised. It can be stated that it gave the first blow to the old rigid determinism of Laplace, and it will perhaps give the key to the difference that exists between life and death.

The reader has gathered from the preceding pages that this strange entity is the only *magnitude* of the universe that increases incessantly, if we consider our universe as a closed system.[5]

---

[5] A non-closed or open system, that is, not completely isolated from other systems, could gain "organization" at the expense of the contiguous systems. That is why a man, for example, cannot be considered as isolated. If he were he would soon die and would be very quickly disorganized. Yet he is a clear example of complete irreversibility.

Every phenomenon, every reaction, results in an increase of entropy. A lighted match, a little boiling water, contribute to degrade, irreversibly, part of the thermic capital of our world, according to Tait's picturesque phrase, which was so well developed by Bernard Brunhes.[6] We have shown that irreversibility was the general rule. Entropy is the measure of this irreversibility.

Entropy expresses the universal trend toward disorder. The evolution of the universe tends toward a state characterized by complete homogeneity, symmetry, and isotropy. No point of the universe will be distinguishable from any other when this state is reached, as the points will all possess the same properties. Time and space will no longer have any meaning. It is in this sense that we must understand the word "disorder." Perfect equilibrium will reign, temperature will be uniform, entropy will be at its maximum.

This is the orthodox, classical opinion. It is clear that it raises objections of a sentimental, aesthetic, and spiritual order. But a great many of these objections fall, if we agree on the meaning of the word "disorder." I will refer to it again later. It is not certain that organization, from the point of view of evolution, should be considered in the same terms as organization in the sense of entropy. In our current language, the disorder in question corresponds more to order, as understood by a good housekeeper. The notion of scale enters into play, and we must remember that the universe appears to us the way it does only because of the infinite number of dissymmetries. Scientifically, we must not forget that we should not extrapolate to the limit, as our observations cover but a very restricted period of time.

The moment just gone by is characterized by more

[6] Bernard Brunhes. *Le dégradation de l'Energie*, Flammarion, Paris.

order than will ever exist in the system under consideration. Complete, perfect order must then have reigned at the origin of things. Oddly enough, this is in accord with all religions.

In a thermodynamic sense, order is only conceived as the antithesis of "disorder" and disorder implies disorganization, complete leveling and suppression of all the dissymmetries that generate forces, work, phenomena. It is an absolutely homogeneous chaos. In religious terminology the word chaos has another meaning, for it contains potentially all the forces of the universe. But above this chaos the Bible admits the existence of an organizing force, the Word. It is in the Word that the regulating power, the will that generates dissymmetries, resides.

But entropy signifies something more, and this something more is of fundamental importance: it gives us the direction of the flow of physical time.

In ordinary life we have consciousness, we have habits, we have birth and death.[7] But we have no landmark in the physical universe. I mean by this that if the time of the universe should suddenly flow backwards, if events should be reversed, none of our physical laws would cease to apply. There would simply be a change of signs.* A pure intelligence, an ideal scientist, might not even notice the change, and simply think that he had used the wrong signs up till then.

I said that we had no landmark, but that is false. We have one, namely entropy. Entropy, as Eddington aptly puts it, is the signpost for time in the physical world. It is the only one. Indeed, as we have seen, entropy establishes the irreversibility of the universe. An isolated system can

[7] See my preceding book, *Biological Time*, Macmillan, New York, 1937, in which I showed the essential difference between the time of things, physical time, and the physiological time in which we live.

* EDITOR'S NOTE: Plus and minus.

never again be in the same state in which it is at a given moment. Entropy can only increase. The proof that it could decrease would indicate that irreversibility is not absolute, that phenomena can evolve in one direction or in another, and the signpost would be meaningless.

The preceding pages have, I hope, convinced the reader of the fundamental importance of the second law of thermodynamics, and of the notion of entropy, in our actual interpretation of the phenomena of nature and their concatenation. These concepts are the cornerstone of our modern macroscopic science. On the other hand, the theory of wave mechanics, the mechanics of subatomic elements, was able to explain a certain number of facts that had been mysterious up till then (the conflict between optics based on the undulations of ether, and the quantum theory, for example). To accomplish this, however, it was forced to introduce new concepts and laws, based on different phenomena on our scale of observation. The transition between the two sciences—the science of atoms and molecules, of macroscopic phenomena, and the science of elementary particles, electrons and others—must exist if we are to conform to our current logic, to the principle of the unity of science. Atoms are composed of electrons, protons, and neutrons. The laws that apply to them must, in some way or other, be connected with our classical laws.

Now the principle of the increase of entropy, by its very generality, is particularly adapted to the study of this transition. This is a crucial problem, and its gravity can escape no one. We must establish the continuity between the two universes that are still separated: the universe of molecules and phenomena in which our existence unfolds, which we have already codified in a satisfactory manner, and the underlying universe of electrons, undisputed base of the first but subject to different laws. We must be able to pass from one to another and any gap of continuity is inconceivable. This problem is not yet solved. It remains like a gaping breach in the arrogant edifice of our science. Some research work has been done on it and a brilliant young Japanese physicist, Satosi Watanabe, a pupil of Louis de Broglie, studied it at length. He published a most interesting pamphlet, which I will briefly summarize.[8]

Our psychological life is a continuous duration. As Bergson said, "it is the uninterrupted progression of the past, which gnaws at the future, and swells as it advances." Our past exists integrally in our present. Our duration is not a point that replaces another on a line, but the prolongation of the entire past conserved in the present.[9]

[8] Satosi Watanabe, *Le deuxieme Théorème de la Thermodynamique et la Mécanique Ondulatoire,* Coll. Hermann & Cie, Paris, 1936.

[9] This constant accumulation has a certain analogy with entropy. But it clearly differs from it in other respects. Indeed, entropy grows at the expense of organization and order, whereas our psychological life tends toward a more and more perfect organization. Entropy levels inequalities, effaces values; whereas psychological evolution is apt to increase them. The hypothesis could be made that everything apparently takes place as though order, with respect to entropy, were replaced, as the human being evolves, by a more and more complex organization in a domain that escapes statistical laws, a realm of individual actions that does not obey the laws of energy we have formulated. Thus the march of the physical universe in the direction of inert chaos, and of total void, would be compensated by the parallel progression of an imponderable spiritual universe, whose order and perfection would rise from the ashes of the material world. At the beginning there would have been a complete, ideal, energetic order, and an utter spiritual void. By degrees energetic order was degraded and consciousness, that marvelous consciousness that enables us to conceive the evolution of the universe, was born progressively. Finally in a cold, chaotic, annihilated universe, where physical action will no longer be possible, a perfect spiritual order, free from all material chains, will exist. The primitive and purely material order would result finally in an order of higher quality and end. . . .

This philosophical fairy tale is open to so many evident objections that it would be better not to express them, especially as we can no more "prove" that it is true than we can "prove" that it is untrue. It is a curious fact that, if the variation of the two contrary processes is expressed by two numbers, *the sum is constant.* This leads us to the Buddhistic concept of the mystic number, the meaning of which is obscure when only one evolution is considered, but which is explained by the aforementioned concept.

The irreversibility of our internal duration can be deduced from the survival of the past. For if we advanced in the opposite direction along this duration it would be a continuous impoverishment of the ego, instead of the insertion of the past into the present.[10]

Briefly, our internal duration implies a one-way direction in our evolution. This being admitted, we can ask if there is a counterpart of this unidirectional flow in physical time. We have seen that the second law of thermodynamics is the only one that expresses an asymmetrical proposition with respect to the two directions of the flow of time. It is, therefore, the only physical theorem that can indicate the one-way direction in the flow of physical time.

The atomic concept in physics leads us to demonstrate this thermodynamic theorem by means of elementary theorems, namely, mechanical and electromagnetic theorems. *But it is known that classical mechanics and the electromagnetic theory are completely reversible in relation to time.*

As we are convinced that wave mechanics must be the very foundation of all physical theories (otherwise it would have no meaning), we are naturally led to ask ourselves the following question: How can we reconcile the reversibility of wave mechanics with the irreversibility of thermodynamics?

"There is only one key of reconciliation," declares Satosi Watanabe, "it is the *statistical* consideration of the results of wave mechanics. There is a great difference between classical statistical mechanics, and statistical mechanics based on wave mechanics."

---

[10] Other arguments could be found by considering physiological time, measured by the velocity of the cicatrization of wounds. (See: Lecomte du Noüy, *Biological Time.*) The reversibility of tissue reparation, or of memory, is inconceivable.

Above all, and this is an observation of the utmost importance that did not escape the young Japanese scientist, it should be noted that an absolutely irreversible phenomenon appears in wave mechanics: *"It is the process of observation which influences the statistical state of the systems."*

The influence of observation (Heisenberg's principle of indeterminacy) is not taken into account in classical statistical mechanics. But we must not lose sight of the relative and subjective character of our interpretations by means of the laws of large numbers, and of the fact that the mind that conceived them, inasmuch as it is the support of our psychological life, is subjected to physiological and psychological time, both subordinated to an absolute irreversibility.

"This irreversibility of observation (in the case of wave mechanics)," says Watanabe, "seems to have some relation to the irreversibility of psychological duration. The two states, one before and the other after the observation, do not, indeed, correspond to two different points on the axis of time. This irreversible process of observation is nothing else but the form of the evolution of our knowledge of the determined object."

If Watanabe only sees one key of reconciliation, it is because he refuses to think in anything but an orthodox, classical fashion. Another key exists, which is equally hypothetical but not more so. It is the key furnished by "Maxwell's demon." * Science refuses to use it before having exhausted all other possible stratagems—and its resources are by no means exhausted.

* EDITOR'S NOTE: Named after James Clerk Maxwell, famous British scientist of the 19th century. Maxwell's "demon" was later termed "anti-chance" by Eddington.

We have ascertained that, in our material macroscopic universe (the world on our scale of observation, the world of our phenomena and of our science) only *a human concept* could indicate the direction of the flow of time. On the other hand, we cannot be mistaken as to the direction of the flow of physiological and psychological time inside of us. In the first case, the problem can only be solved by making the observer intervene either by the observation itself, or by the logical consequences that he derives from his observations (law of the increase of entropy). In the other case, the problem is directly solved by our consciousness, the most direct object of our knowledge. Statistical laws can be applied in the first case, but they apply poorly in the second, and it is not certain that individual actions, fluctuations, do not play a preponderant part. In the first case there is no derogation to the second principle; in the second—the case of life and thought—derogations can be admitted. The appreciation of the flow of time, outside and inside of us, does not, therefore, rest on the same mechanisms, but in the end they both depend on our consciousness and our intelligence, and we were justified in describing physical time, the time of the inert universe, as a conceptual time in opposition to real, to living time.[11]

[11] Lecomte du Noüy, *Biological Time, loc. cit.,* p. 145 *et al.*

A CRITICAL SURVEY

Argument

By decreasing the time in which an event can occur the probability for its occurrence decreases. Borel's example of the "type-writing" monkeys is the most celebrated illustration of highly improbable cases.

When we calculate the probability for the formation of a dissymmetrical protein molecule we find that the required time is so great that it exceeds the age of the universe. The probability that "Maxwell's demon," or what Eddington called "anti-chance," intervened is much greater. To produce the number of protein molecules required to create life this anti-chance would have to act systematically.

The formation of a cell is even more mysterious and introduces four fundamental problems: the creation of a new dissymmetry on a higher scale; the appearance of an individual system limited in time; the necessity for this system to live at the expense of the surrounding medium; and the possibility for this system to create another system identical to itself.

The statistics employed in the subatomic realm, different from those used in the case of molecules or particles of matter, suppress all individuality. How, then, does individual character in physics as well as in biology arise?

5

A CRITICAL SURVEY

CALCULUS OF PROBABILITIES · STATISTICS

> The complex is not always profound; but the profound is not necessarily simple.
>
> —THE AUTHOR

WE NOW have a superficial idea of how the law of large numbers enables us to interpret the universe or, more exactly, to translate and foresee quantitatively the reactions unloosed by the external world. From this, we have deduced the subjective and human notion of phenomenon, which depends essentially on the scale of observation. We have pointed out some of the difficulties raised by the unification of science, even in pure physics.

Certain examples were given so that the reader might understand the significance of statistical laws, and the legitimacy of the calculus of probabilities. These examples were necessarily simple; much simpler than reality ever is. We could thus understand the mechanism of the calculus. But probabilities are usually "compound." They are computed with the help of the following theorem, which I will partially quote from Borel to show that the calculus can lend itself to more complex cases.

"When the event, the probability of which we seek, consists in the successive occurrence of two events, the unknown probability is equal to the product of the probability of the first of these events, by the probability that the second will take place when the first has taken place." Theoretically, this is simple, but it is less so in practice when we have to deal with more than two events.

We will now try to examine the real meaning of certain words and ideas. We will begin by the words "possible" and "impossible," which the calculus of probabilities has struck from the dictionary. As we have seen, they have been replaced by "high probability" and "high improbability." If the probability of an event is infinitely small, it is equivalent to the *practical* impossibility of its taking place. The theoretical possibility always exists; but it can be so slight that it is equivalent to a quasi certitude of the contrary.[1]

Different examples have been given to illustrate highly improbable cases. But we must remember that the word "highly," as well as the expressions "very great" or "very slight" have only a relative meaning. Only a number signifies something, and a number expressing a probability corresponds to precise data and to a determined interval of time. It is evident that if, when stating a problem, we decrease the time allotted to the experiment, the probability of this event decreases. On the contrary, by increasing it infinitely, the probability increases. We will come back to this subject farther on.

The three most celebrated examples are those of Jeans, Borel, and Perrin. The one given by Jeans can be expressed in the following words: If a saucepan of water is

---

[1] ". . . Probability and certitude have no common measure," said Borel. (*Le Hasard*, p. 231.) Equivalence does not signify identity.

put on the fire to boil, there is one probability that the water will freeze. Borel used the following allegory to give a concrete idea of the probability that in a vessel (a) containing a gas and communicating with another vessel, (b) there would be a change in the composition of the gas mixture of the order of one hundred thousandth, during a very short lapse of time: "Let us suppose that a million monkeys have been trained to strike at random on the keys of a million typewriters, and that these monkeys work ardently 10 hours a day under the supervision of illiterate overseers. Let us suppose further, that these illiterate overseers assemble the pages, and bind them together in volumes, and that at the end of a year these volumes contain an exact copy, in all languages, of all the books preserved in the world's richest libraries." "To suppose," adds Borel, "that the change thus produced (in the composition of the gas mixture) subsists for several seconds amounts to the same as to admit that our army of monkey typists, working for several years, always under the same conditions, will furnish every day the exact copy of all the magazines, books, and newspapers, which will appear the corresponding day of the week after, on the whole surface of the globe, and of all the words which will be pronounced by all men on that same day. It is simpler to say that these improbable fluctuations are impossible." [2]

The preceding lines give a clear idea of the true value of statistical laws applied to simple phenomena such as the equi-partition of pressure in communicating vessels, or the homogeneity of the mixture, and also of the complexity of the events that can enter into a calculus of probabilities; the probability that the books, newspapers, and words should be really reconstituted.

[2] E. Borel, *Le Hasard*. Alcan, p. 164, 1914, *op. cit.*

The third example is given by Perrin. We have already alluded to it in the preceding pages: it is the spontaneous rise of a body. In reference to this we shall quote an ingenious and sensible comment by Borel.[3] "In a sense, however, we can affirm that we will never scientifically observe a phenomenon as slightly probable as, for example, the spontaneous rise of a brick to the height of a first floor, through the action of the Brownian movement. Indeed, if observers stated that they had witnessed such a phenomenon, we would have to admit that they had been victims of a collective hallucination or that, for some other reason, their testimony did not correspond to an objective reality; for, no matter how much confidence we had in them, this eventuality would still be much more probable than the production of the event in question."

This observation singularly restricts the practical scope of certain conclusions that one might be tempted to deduce from the calculus of probabilities, and limits the extension of the word "possible."

Indeed, what do the words "possible" and "impossible" signify in reality? Have they an absolute, or only a relative value? It seems that only a relative human meaning can be logically attributed to them, not only with respect to a human life, but with respect to thinking humanity, which adopts and makes its own the acquisitions, discoveries, and ideas of all its members, in order to edify what constitutes the intellectual capital of the species. From this point of view, humanity acts like one single being endowed with memory, and that is the condition of progress.

Moreover, we must remember that the word "impossible" can be applied to two kinds of events. One kind

[3] E. Borel, Mécanique statistique classique. Fasc. III., p. 146. Paris. Gauthier-Villars, 1925.

cannot be dealt with by means of the calculus of probabilities, for simple basic and structural reasons: for example, the impossibility of throwing seven with a single die; and the other, for more complex reasons: the impossibility for man to escape death.

To consider the death of an individual as a "highly probable" event is a mere play on words, without significance. We do not gain anything by saying that the probability of such a phenomenon is equal to one.

When does the probability of an event correspond practically to a certitude? When is it theoretically identified with it? I know that a pure mathematician will always affirm that a fact, even though very improbable, can nevertheless take place. As we have just seen, the practical criticism of this reasoning was made by Borel, but the theoretical criticism is worth attempting, for when we push things to the extreme, as all mathematicians are authorized to do, we are in danger of arriving involuntarily at false conclusions, which borrow their prestige from that of mathematics.[4]

We must not forget that, as Karl Pearson said, mathematics is nothing but a system of mental stenography and that at the end of all the calculations in the world, we can never find anything else than what we put into the equations from which we started.

The beauty of the calculus of probabilities, the admirable precision it enables us to reach, the astounding conclusions we derive from it, do not authorize us to affirm

[4] "The main reason why the mathematician has beaten his rivals is that we have allowed him to dictate the terms of the competition. The fate of every theory of the universe is decided by a numerical test. Does the sum come out right? I am not sure that the mathematician understands this world of ours better than the poet and the mystic. Perhaps it is only that he is better at sums." (Sir Arthur Eddington, *New Pathways of Science,* Cambridge University Press, p. 324, 1935.

that it alone can interpret all the facts of nature. We know that it is sometimes possible to interpret them differently, and we have already seen, in the preceding pages, that its application to the phenomena of life raises difficulties that impose the greatest circumspection.

Man has a tendency to admire the works produced by his brain more than the brain itself. He is inclined to forget their origin, and to confer on them a superhuman authority. In so doing, he yields to his innate desire to believe and does not always realize the extent to which he has become a slave of this belief in his reason. Faith in the permanence of an established order—the foundation of science—and faith in the unlimited power of the methods issued from his brain, such is the creed of a certain number of scientists of today.

At a lecture followed by a debate, on "The Limits of Legitimate Inference," which I gave at the Collège de France in 1938, one of these scientists criticized the restrictions I had made on the possible application of the second principle of thermodynamics to living organisms. Being a physicist, who had never studied a living cell, the only argument he could muster in defense of his theories was the following: "I will never believe that there can be systems to which the second principle does not apply."

I asked for facts, he answered by a profession of faith. It is curious to observe that the sectarian spirit of the Middle Ages can, nowadays, be found on the other side of the fence and that it has lost none of its original vigor.

To come back to our subject, let us try to perceive the meaning of certain calculated probabilities and to see how legitimate it is to apply these methods to other than general physical domains.

First of all, the significance of the number expressed by

the powers of 10. Even the cultivated reader, unless he is a scientist, does not always fully realize the exact figures represented by this extremely practical method. It is an abbreviation for large numbers; 10 is represented as 10^1, 100 as 10^2, 1,000,000 as 10^6, 1,000,000,000 as 10^9. The upper small number indicates the number of zeros following the 1, and is called the exponent. Fractional values are indicated by a minus sign in front of the exponent. It is not easy to conceive the extreme smallness of an atom, or of a molecule. We know, however, that a cubic centimeter (less than the volume of a thimble) of gas at $0°$C. and at the "normal" pressure, contains 3×10^{19} molecules, or 30,-000,000,000,000,000,000. To express the *total* number of electrons and protons contained, not only in the terrestrial globe but in the sun, the planets, and all the worlds of the universe visible through the telescope, that is, all the Milky Way and the nebulae beyond, we only have to write 2×10^{79}. I do not guarantee the absolute precision of this number but it was obtained by two different methods that check each other and that both seem plausible.[5] Thus 2×10^{79} represents the *total number* of corpuscles in Einstein's universe. It does not seem as though a number, followed by 79 zeros, could suffice to express it, when 19 zeros are necessary to express the number of molecules in a cubic centimeter of air!

If we have the fancy to express astronomical distances, no longer in light years nor in kilometers, nor even in meters, but in thousandths of a millimeter, in microns, we

[5] First, by the theory of Abbé Lemaitre, which leads to the conclusion that the total quantity of matter in the universe is about 10^{22} times that of the sun. If a galaxy of average size contains 10 billions of stars (our Milky Way) this would give about a thousand billion galaxies (10^{12}). And, secondly, by Eddington's method. (*Loc. cit.*, p. 221.) However, Milne's new theory does not lead to a limited number of corpuscles for the universe, nor to the possibility of computing them.

shall reach only very modest figures: the distance from the sun to the earth, 150×10^{15} microns (150 million kilometers); limit of the solar system, 5.8×10^{18} microns (5.8×10^9 kilometers); nearest star, 40×10^{21} microns; nearest galaxy, 10×10^{27} microns. Original circumference of the universe, 65×10^{30} microns. It would take about 20 billion years to cover this last distance, if we traveled at the velocity of light (186,000 miles per second).

It is conceded that the beginning of the cooling of the earth's crust cannot go back more than 2 billion years: 2×10^9 years. The first rocks appeared about 1 billion 300 million years ago (1.3×10^9). These are extreme valuations.

Expressed in centuries, this gives 2×10^7 centuries for the period of cooling. Now in a century, there are less than 10^5 days. This means that less than 2×10^{12} days have passed. In a day there are less than 10^5 seconds; therefore, less than 2×10^{17} seconds have elapsed. This last number, therefore, contains *all the past history* of the terrestrial globe, namely, our whole human reality.

To obtain slightly larger numbers, we must turn to the age of the sun which, according to modern theories, cannot exceed 5×10^{12} years (5 trillion) or 5×10^{20} seconds.

Let us consider a probability of the order of 10^{-73}. This is the probability, in an experiment dealing with 1000 grains, that 700 white grains and 300 black, or vice versa, would appear in this order after being shaken. This means that it would be necessary to shake 10^{73} times, so as to have, on an average, one chance for this combination to appear. (Calculation made according to Stirling's formula.)

Even if we admit the possibility of 100 billion shakes per second, or 10^{11}, during 1 billion billion centuries—a period of time 100 million times greater than the age of the sun—it would only add up to 10^{39} shakes instead of 10^{73}. The shaking would have to continue for billions of billions of centuries.*

It is impossible, because of the immense complexity of the problem, to lay the foundation of a calculation that would establish the probability of the spontaneous appearance of life on earth. However, we can approach this by simplifying the problem and calculating the probability of the appearance of certain essential molecules. The elementary molecules of living organisms are all characterized by an important asymmetry. Asymmetry can be expressed by a number between 0.5 and 1. The number 1 corresponds to a maximum dissymmetry (in the example of the black and white grains, all the white on one side, and all the black on the other). The number 0.5 corresponds to a more uniform and more probable distribution; an equal number of black and white grains on either side. The most probable fluctuations are grouped about the degree of symmetry 0.5 (see table, p. 92). These calculations were made by Guye for a molecule with a degree of dissymmetry equal to 0.9, where m (the half-number of constituent atoms) is equal to 1000. In order to simplify the question considerably, he made the supposition that there are only two kinds of atoms. There would thus be 2000 atoms in all.

The atomic weight of these atoms being considered equal to 10 (another simplification), the molecular weight is 20,000. This figure is lower than that of the simplest proteins (34,500). The number of molecules to a cubic centimeter is 3×10^{19} (the average concentration of proteins in the liquids of the organism is about 3×10^{18}) and the probability of the appearance of a configuration of dissym-

---

* EDITOR'S NOTE: It should be pointed out that the author intended this to be taken as an illustrative calculation and not as an all-embracing proof that there is no way in which a protein could have arisen through chance alone.

metrical degree equal to 0.9 would be 2.02×10^{-321}. The volume of substance necessary for such a probability to take place defies imagination. It would be that of a sphere with a radius so great that light would take 10^{82} years to traverse it, a volume incomparably greater than all the universe, comprising the farthest galaxies (more than one sextillion sextillion sextillion times greater).

The probability that a single molecule of high dissymmetry can be formed by the action of the thermal agitation is practically nil. Indeed, if we suppose 500 trillion shakes per second (5×10^{14}), which corresponds to the order of magnitude of light periodicity, we find that the time needed, *on an average,* to form one such molecule of a degree of dissymmetry equal to 0.9 in a material volume equal to that of our terrestrial globe is still about 10^{243} billions of years. We remind the reader that the probable age of the earth from the time it began to cool is of the order of 2 billion or 2×10^9 years, and that this "accident" must have occurred in the first billion years, as we have reason to believe that life existed on our globe a billion years ago.[6]

When we consider the immensity of the numbers expressed by the powers of 10, it becomes evident that *exponents superior to 100 correspond to values that no longer hold significance for the human mind.*

A probability which, in order to have one mean chance of manifesting itself, requires much longer than the estimated duration of our globe, or of our planetary system—even when we admit numerous reactions, shakings, or experiments per second—would logically seem to be an impossibility in the human sense.

On the other hand, we can always argue the fact that

[6] See: E. Gagnebin, Bull. Soc. Vaud. Sc. Nat., vol. 58, N. 234, 1934.

the chances, however slight, nevertheless exist, and that the rare configuration need not take place at the end of billions of centuries. It may happen at the very beginning, in the first second. Not only is this quite in accord with the calculation, but we can even admit that the phenomenon will take place twice in succession, and then practically never again.

The problem becomes strangely complicated when, instead of calculating the probability of the appearance of a single highly dissymmetrical molecule, we attempt to calculate the probability of a *continuous succession* of similar configurations. The resulting figures are so high that astronomical figures become completely negligible in comparison.

Numbers such as 10^{600} or 10^{-600}, which we obtain when considering simply 1000 grains or 1000 atoms belonging to only two different categories (black and white), already represent absolutely inconceivable numbers and are the mathematical and elegant expression of our total ignorance.

Immeasurably larger numbers would be required to explain the appearance of life on earth by means of our actual scientific concepts. One of the immediate consequences to be derived from this way of looking at things is the improbability that a similar conjuncture has ever occurred in any other part of the universe, no matter what its age. There are then very great chances that life—such as we know it—exists only on our globe and will never again appear when, due to its inevitable cooling, or some other kind of unforeseen cataclysm, the world will have ceased to shelter it.

Strictly speaking, it is therefore highly improbable that thermal agitation succeeded by chance alone in producing

molecules—or *even one single* highly dissymmetrical molecule—such as the proteins that are invariably found at the
base of even the simplest living organisms—spores and
microbes. We must, therefore, logically seek another active element; radiation or something else. Or else admit
the intervention of Maxwell's demon, the "cheater" whom
Eddington so aptly called "anti-chance."

The probability of an "anti-chance" intervening is infinitely higher than the opposite probability.

Nevertheless, we are forced to admit that as soon as the
world had cooled to a temperature compatible with the
stability of proteins, that is, below 150° (certain spores
resist at 120°), an event took place that was so improbable
that, if it had not taken place immediately, it could never
have taken place at all; so improbable that it will never
again take place anywhere in the universe, otherwise we
might doubt that its appearance was due solely to chance.
This event, in itself rigorously unique, is the production of
one protein molecule, that is, *one* of the bricks indispensable to the construction of a human being.

There is, however, a serious objection, based on our lack
of knowledge of the degree of complexity of a protein
molecule, to all the above arguments. The only answer can
be that this molecule was highly dissymmetrical and that its
basic properties depend on its dissymmetry.[7] On the other
hand, we must remind the reader that the problem has
been considerably simplified: first by admitting that only
two kinds of atoms entered into the construction of a molecule, whereas we know that there are at least four, and
generally five, namely, carbon, hydrogen, nitrogen, oxygen

[7] See Louis Pasteur. (*Letters.*) "Life is dominated by dissymmetrical
actions. I am even inclined to believe that all living species are, in their
structure and outward forms, primarily functions of cosmic dissymmetry."

—besides these, there is sulphur in albumin (probably sixteen atoms per molecule), iron in hemoglobin, copper in hemocyanin; second, by admitting that a molecule is composed of 2000 atoms, whereas one of the simplest of the protein molecules, egg albumin, has about 4448 atoms.[8]

But we can also argue that there is no proof that the original protein was as complicated as are those of today, and that the primitive organisms were built with a simple "brick." Unfortunately, egg albumin or a similar structure of the same molecular weight of 34,500 seems to be the constitutive element in the structure of *all* other proteins whose molecular weights are integral multiples of this number: 34,500. For example: serum albumin 69,000 (factor 2), serum globulin 138,000 (factor 4), etc. Moreover, it is a very curious fact that the *simplest and least evolved organisms in the animal kingdom are the ones that possess proteins of the highest molecular weight.* The hemocyanin (blood-pigment) of certain gastropods (snails) has a molecular weight greater than 5,000,000 (Svedberg) which varies with the seasons.[9]

We cannot, however, state definitely that a body endowed with the properties of proteins did not exist in the beginning: an assemblage of about 20 molecules of amino acids, for instance, with a molecular weight about one-

[8] Probable formula of egg albumin (Osborne):

$$2 (C_{696} H_{1125} N_{175} S_8 O_{220})$$

which gives 4448 atoms instead of 2000.

[9] Kurt G. Stern, at Yale, employing the technique of Arne Tiselius, obtained molecules extracted from the muscles of the heart, to which he attributes a molecular weight greater than 100,000,000 (*Science,* Vol. 88, p. 12 (supplement), 1938). We cannot guarantee the exactitude of this figure, but it is certain that the molecular weights of proteins constituting viruses (tobacco-mosaic, rabbit papilloma) are greater than 10,000,000. (Wyckoff, Stanley.)

fourth of that of egg albumin. But we have no scientific proof of this. On the other hand, the kidney and liver of very elementary animals, such as the limulus (horseshoe crab) and those of more highly evolved mammals show no specific difference in their functions.

Consequently, there is nothing improbable in these calculations, which represent an extremely simplified possibility, according to recent chemical data. And it must be admitted that the questions we raised were entirely hypothetical.

Let us, therefore, admit that, by an extraordinary but quite ʿ ʾ missible chance, *one* molecule was formed. This isolated molecule would have been useless. We are forced to conceive the production of several grams of proteins, of several billion billion molecules.

As the calculus of probability shows that the production of one single molecule, by chance alone, is inconceivably rare, we are faced with the necessity of introducing an external cause, also due to chance, but capable of influencing in a certain direction the common laws of chance governing thermal agitation. Indeed, we have seen that, according to these laws, the probability of the appearance of a single dissymmetrical molecule was so slight that it only had one chance in a space of time much greater than the age of the sun, or the age of the universe. To admit that this phenomenon could have taken place billions of times, in an extremely short space of time, *is to completely deny the possibility of applying the calculus of probability to this problem.*

We must, therefore, bring in a "foreign cause." But this foreign cause must be of a special nature, which should facilitate our task in a certain measure by limiting our field of investigations. Indeed, this "cause" is characterized by

the fact that it has never manifested itself in the laboratory. This enables us to eliminate a fairly large number of
possible causes and, in any event, those that would seem
at first glance to be the most plausible. It has *never* been
possible to synthesize a protein despite the repeated efforts
made by some of the most brilliant chemists. However,
much less than a century has elapsed since this problem
was first tackled, and it will probably be solved as a result
of the important progress recently made by the synthesis
of certain vitamins and hormones. Nevertheless, it is permissible to think that the conditions that prevailed at the
period of the earth's cooling, when the "cause" acted, can
no longer exist today. During the period of our world's
youth, there may have been a concurrence of circumstances that will never occur again; in the same way the
human body cannot effectuate the same syntheses at a
mature age as in the embryonic stage.

We are once more reduced to conjectures lacking scientific value. We can speak of "radiation," of an "electric
state of the atmosphere," etc., but we do not know how a
"radiation" or an "electric state" could have played the
part of organizer and systematic creator of dissymmetry.
It is simpler to say we do not know.

We are forced to admit this state of affairs which, from
the point of view of our statistical interpretation of phenomena, is singularly disturbing. We must not forget that
the increase of entropy demands that the evolution of an
isolated system should always progress in the direction of
the highest probability (see p. 99). Now, we have shown
above that a state that is less symmetrical than the preceding state is less probable than the first. When a complex,
having a greater degree of dissymmetry than the elements
that compose it, is formed, we are, therefore, in apparent

contradiction with the second principle of thermodynamics.

Two hypotheses are possible: either entropy decreases, which may happen in the case of a very rare fluctuation— but then we are not dealing with a systematic phenomenon, such as the production of millions of molecules, or we cannot consider the system in question as isolated. In the latter case, we must bring in some action foreign to the system; an action having a role exactly opposed to that of chance, and which creates dissymmetry, whereas chance would tend to suppress it. We fall back on an "anti-chance," and Maxwell's demon.

The dilemma is extremely embarrassing and we cannot escape it. Momentarily, we are faced by a mystery, but our actual ignorance cannot last very long, and we must hope that this problem will be solved in a century or two.

We must, therefore, admit as an unverifiable truth that proteins were created as soon as the cooling of the earth's crust made this possible. Chance must now again be called in to explain the formation of the first living element: a cell. The problem had already become more complicated when we tried to explain the production of proteins in series, but now words completely fail to express our incompetence. We have only a slender thread to guide us, the increase of entropy; and we have at our disposal only one tool, the calculus of probabilities based on chance. Now, we insist upon the fact that the increase of entropy, in an isolated system, can only correspond to an ever-increasing disorder, and a decrease of dissymmetry. In the study of the most elementary manifestations, not only of life, but of the materials that compose it, *we face creations of dissymmetry*.

As far as proteins are concerned, our ignorance of the

chemistry of large molecules is not surprising when we consider the small number of years that have been consecrated to this study. We are still in the first stages. But the cell introduces a problem which, at first sight, seems to be fourfold:

1st. Creation of a new dissymmetry on a higher scale. Indeed, it is evident that the presence of a cell containing complex individual elements, such as the nucleus, and composed for the most part of protein molecules adsorbed in a polarized layer at interfaces, constitutes an important dissymmetry. We shall come back to this later.

2nd. Appearance of an individual and closed, even if not isolated, system, *limited in time*: it is born and dies. If it does not die it divides itself in two. But it only persists in its actual state for a determined length of time: *it is a cyclic phenomenon*.

3rd. Necessity for this system to live at the expense of the surrounding medium, which entails assimilation and disassimilation (metabolism and katabolism), namely chemical reactions of enzymic nature.

4th. Possibility for this system to create, in one way or another, a second system identical to itself.

I have not mentioned the fact that certain isolated cells are endowed with movement for two reasons: first, because a great number of them are immobile; and second, because, as far as the amoebae are concerned, a physico-chemical explanation can be given. But the above four problems are sufficient for the present. We shall examine them in order:

1st. Creation of a new dissymmetry. The fact itself is unquestionable, but, with the help of a hypothesis that I propounded long ago, I will try to explain how this increase in dissymmetry corresponds, under certain very particular conditions, to a state that is more probable than isotropic distribution.[10]

In previous experiments,[11] I showed that proteins, without exception, possessed the property of decreasing the surface tension of water. Following the second principle of thermodynamics, a system always tends toward the state of equilibrium which corresponds to the minimum free energy compatible with the total energy of the system. The free energy of a liquid, or a solution, is a function of its surface tension. Since, for an unknown reason, proteins are capable of lowering the surface tension of the water in which they are in solution, they will go to the surface of the liquid, or to the surface of separation, following the second principle and Gibbs' law and will be adsorbed or fixed. The free energy of the system will thus be decreased.

If we consider a droplet of the solution, and imagine that it is isolated in the air for a few moments, the proteins will immediately be adsorbed at the surface, thus determining the formation of a film or membrane, the *first manifestation of individuality*. Since the second principle is respected in this case, we can state that under certain determined conditions the cell form is the most probable configuration of equilibrium of a protein solution.

The increase of dissymmetry due to the fact that an "individual" has been formed and to the further fact that the protein molecules are adsorbed in a polarized layer (that is, symmetrically juxtaposed like the bricks of a wall) is counterbalanced by the important decrease in the free energy of the system. In this case, it can, therefore, be admitted that the balance is in favor of the increase of

[10] Lecomte du Noüy, *Surface Equilibria of Biological and Organic Colloids.* The Chemical Catalog Co. (Reinhold Publishing Corp.), New York, 1926.

[11] Lecomte du Noüy, C.R.Ac, Sc. 174,962,1258 (1922) and *loc. cit.*

entropy, although we have no way of proving it quantitatively.

The objection can be raised that the reason for the formation of these droplets, capable of transforming themselves into cells—5 to 10 microns in diameter—is not clear. I have answered this by imagining that, in addition to the necessary salts, the seas of the Pre-Cambrian period may have contained proteins in solution, and that the breaking waves formed a mist composed of droplets, a large number of which could have had these dimensions. I also supplied further arguments, which cannot be developed here but to which the reader can refer if he is interested.[12] However, I always realized that even if the thermodynamical explanation seems valid, as far as the formation of a cell is concerned, it cannot explain the appearance of the nucleus and of the vital properties of the whole. A watch case without works does not indicate the time. But we must not be too hard to please, and when, for once, we have the possibility of applying the second principle of thermodynamics to a phenomenon pertaining to life, we must esteem ourselves relatively satisfied.

2nd. Appearance of a system constituting an individual and subjected to a cyclic rhythm.

From now on we shall find ourselves going down a slippery incline, which a number of eminent thinkers have followed without even being aware of it. We shall see that the cycle in question, which extends from birth to death, or to cellular subdivision, is a function of temperature and subject to van't Hoff's law. This law can be expressed in the following manner: a rise in the normal temperature of 10 degrees centigrade suffices to double approximately the velocity of a chemical reaction.

[12] See footnote 10, p. 132.

Generally the velocity of reaction is more than doubled. It is multiplied by a coefficient that varies, according to the case, between 2.3 and 2.7. On an average it is equal to 2.5.

We were able to show, in collaboration with A. H. Ebeling, that a phenomenon as complex as the cicatrization of wounds also obeyed this law.[13] These phenomena are, therefore, fundamentally conditioned by facts pertaining to chemistry.

Consequently, we will be tempted to say that the cyclic phenomenon in question obeys a statistical law and is, therefore, subject to the second principle. It contributes to the increase of entropy; it is "more probable" (in the Boltzmannian sense of the word) and has its place in the statistical interpretation of evolution. So the question is solved and we will pass on to another problem. This is the incline I mentioned but, alas, there is a nail in it. Unless we see it in time, we may regret the consequences. Indeed, when we say that this phenomenon, like many others in biology, obeys van't Hoff's law, it simply means that we are in the presence of a large enough number of molecules for the statistical laws to apply to their dissociating collisions, to their activations, and therefore to their velocity of reactions.

When the temperature is raised, the number of dissociating collisions that conditions the velocity of the reaction increases. It follows that the velocity increases. But this is the limit of its action, and nothing in van't Hoff's law enables us to foresee the existence of a periodical phenomenon. It is true that if the reactions are accelerated the cycle will be shorter. But why is there a cycle? How

[13] A. H. Ebeling: J. Exp. Med. N. Y., Vol. 35, p. 657 (1922), and in Lecomte du Noüy: *Biological Time*, p. 98.

is it that the result of the cycle is an extremely complicated group of phenomena, differing in nature, but classed
together under the name of mitosis?

I cannot, without transgressing the limits of this study,
dwell on this prodigious phenomenon, but we need only
open an elementary book on cytology and cast an eye on
the mitotic figures to realize that we are faced by a series
of rigorously coordinated facts, and that this coordination,
on our scale of observation, seems to have no relation to the
reactions that take place on the molecular scale. This
relation probably exists and we may understand it some
day, but we have not yet the faintest conception of it. We
cannot even say that it exists. There is no experimental
proof of it. Anyone who pretends the contrary is either a
visionary or a prevaricator.

The second problem is, therefore, a total deception as
far as our purely statistical hopes are concerned. We lose
contact with entropy as soon as we deal with the coordination of mechanisms on a higher scale, even though this is
not the case for the molecular mechanisms.

3rd. Necessity for this system to live at the expense of
the surrounding medium.

Here we again come up against two series of facts, one
of which can without great difficulty fall into the scope
of physical chemistry and thermodynamics, while the
other, at first glance, presents difficulties that are at the
moment unsolved. Indeed, there are many examples of
growth in the inorganic world: crystals developing in
their mother solution, the artificial cells of Leduc, grow-
ing and taking on the most diverse shapes.

The problem is very much simplified in the case of
crystals; there is no chemical reaction. Under certain
conditions of temperature, pressure, concentration, the

molecules are joined together, following a plan determined by their symmetry; they lose their individuality
by creating their characteristic lattice structure. Crystals,
in solution, grow by impoverishing the medium in which
they bathe. There is no assimilation, no respiration; there
is a reversible change of state. The same elements sometimes tend to agglomerate in different ways, according to
the temperature or pressure. The substances can then
crystallize into different systems. They are said to be
polymorphous, or allotropic. This is the case of sulphur,
carbon, calcium carbonate, silica. Thus there is nothing
in common between the growth of crystals and that of
cells, which is irreversible.

The artificial cells of Leduc represent a much more
complex phenomenon. They are obtained in a very simple manner.[14] The semipermeable membrane that is
formed has a certain resemblance to the cellular "membrane," built up by oriented molecules. They grow in the
mother-solution by making a selection amongst the molecules. This results in remarkable arborescences, resembling certain seaweeds. But, here again, there is no assimilation by digestion, no transformation by hydrolysis of
molecules. There is only an imitation of the growth of a
plant, by means of processes that are sometimes similar
and sometimes different. The pseudamoeboid cells, obtained with a drop of chloroform, likewise demonstrate
the part played by certain physico-chemical phenomena
(interfacial tension) in the amoeboid movements, and in
the process of the absorption of nourishing particles by
the amoeba. We have seen that these phenomena are

[14] S. Leduc, *Essais de Biologie Synthétique.* (Biochem. Ztsch., 1908,
p. 282, in A & A Mary, *ibid.*) and "La Diffusion et l'Osmose." Previous
to this, Böttger (1865), Traube (1866) and Benedikt, R. Dubois, Quincke,
etc.

always present, but everything takes place in the living cell, as though they were coordinated in view of at least one final result: mitosis. In the artificial cells there is nothing of the same nature and the two are no more identical than Vaucanson's automaton duck and a living duck.

The living cell, in order to feed itself, absorbs products different from those that compose it; it decomposes these products or, more exactly, hydrolizes them by means of enzymes or soluble ferments. In other words, it breaks up these materials, which are useless in their original form, and uses the fragments to build up protein and other molecules, which constitute its own substance. These enzymes are specific and can only digest a well-defined category of molecules. We still have only a fragmentary knowledge of their origin. The cell manufactures them out of its own substance.

Certain cells are, moreover, endowed with highly specialized properties. The cells of green plants, for instance, secrete the extraordinary substance called chlorophyll, which fixes carbon directly from the air. The widely prevalent microorganisms, called *Rotifera*, can be completely desiccated and submitted to a temperature of 270°C. below zero (3 degrees above absolute zero). They regain all their activity and mobility as soon as they are given the water they lacked, at the proper temperature. Microbic cells secrete formidable toxins and are sometimes endowed with movement, but these movements are very different from those that can be explained by capillary phenomena (spirochetes for example).

The list of the specific properties of cells would fill an entire volume, beginning with the amoeba and ending up with the pyramidal brain cells, which do not reproduce themselves. The physico-chemical laws, the statistical laws, apply in general, but sometimes with curious, and still incomprehensible, restrictions. *In all cases, these restrictions, these exceptions to the rules, these sometimes slight infractions to our laws, cease to exist as soon as the cell is dead.* For example, Osterhout [15] demonstrated that membranes of the large isolated cells of certain algae of Bermuda show a high electric resistance—from 300 to 600 ohms—as long as the cell is healthy. Any pathological state, determined by a variation in the constitution of the liquid in which it grows (sea water), brings about a decrease in the resistance. This decrease is proportional to the "health" of the cell and, when the cell is dead, the resistance falls to 30 or 40 ohms.

By studying the orientation of the molecules at the surface of the cell's delimitating membrane, we can give a rough and hypothetical explanation of this phenomenon. Indeed, an oriented monomolecular layer acts as an electric condenser. As long as the orientation persists, the outside electric charge impedes the passage of certain ions through the membrane, and this results, macroscopically, in a fairly high electric resistance. Under certain conditions, when the equilibrium of the ions is modified in the cell medium, the orientation of adsorbed molecules can be altered, or the structure of external chemical groups, which determine the polarity, can be changed. The charge of the condenser is less strong and does not oppose itself as energetically to the passage of the ions; the resistance decreases. The depolarization is complete at death, and the only resistance is the normal resistance of the inert membrane. It is a minimum. This explanation, which I proposed at the time of the discovery of Osterhout, who

[15] Osterhout, *Injury, Recovery and Death,* New York, 1926.

was my colleague at the Rockefeller Institute, is only a tentative explanation. It probably contains a certain amount of truth, but it would be difficult to prove experimentally.

4th. Possibility for this system to create, in one way or another, a second system that is identical to the first.

This fourth problem, which is directly connected with the others, is impressive chiefly by its mechanism. The latter reveals a complexity of structure and of properties, even in the simplest cell, which a microscopic examination is powerless to elucidate. It is clearly differentiated from the growth of crystals and artificial cells by the sequence and coordination of the series of phenomena that constitute mitosis.

An organization on a higher scale is superimposed on the chemical and physico-chemical actions that enter into play. We are able to follow certain of its stages through the microscope, without knowing if what we see is not the manifestation, on a perceptible scale, of other similarly coordinated but invisible phenomena, just as the disordered Brownian movements are the resultant, on a higher scale, of the thermal agitation of molecules.

There is an immense gap between the molecular state, subject to disordered thermal agitation, and what we might call the protoplasmic state. Our ignorance on the subject is complete. It is useless to try to apply the rules of the calculus of probabilities to internal cellular phenomena. We would only obtain figures without any significance. We have seen that this calculus, when applied to a relatively simple phenomenon such as the production of one molecule, leads to absurd consequences if an unknown cause, an antichance, is not made to intervene.

The question—what are the probabilities of the ap-

pearance of a cell by pure chance at the period of formation of proteins?—poses a false problem, for it is not
homogeneous. Even if it were homogeneous and contained
only elements of a similar nature, the number of these
elements would be so great, and the configurations so numerous that though arbitrarily simplified to the extreme
—as in the case of the black and white grains—the figures
obtained would exceed all limits. We relapse into miracles,
resembling those of the typewriting monkeys, which are
expressed by a probability of the order of $10^{-2,000,000,000,000}$. A
book of ordinary size contains less than one million letters.
To write out the above figure, it would be necessary to
print two million books containing only zeros, except for
the number 1 at the end of the last page of the last volume.

Now, in the beginning there must have been not only
one but billions of cells. To admit that, once the first cell
was created by chance, the second, as well as the third
and fourth, had to follow by parthenogenesis, as in the
formation of blastulae, is to admit the appearance *ex
nihilo* of a cyclic, systematic, temporal process, which cannot be expressed in terms of the calculus of probabilities.
It is an "absolute beginning." The symbols, employed by
this calculus, only enable us to evaluate the probability
of appearance of a determined state considered statically.
By introducing a kinematic process we therefore lose the
possibility of explaining the creation of cells by chance
alone. The probability, if it could be calculated, that millions of cells (identical or not) could be produced by
chance would give an infinitely smaller figure than the
one mentioned above. Fluctuations of this kind completely
destroy the value of the calculus of probabilities in similar
cases.

It is much simpler to say that, up till now, we have not

been able to furnish a single scientific explanation of life, nor of its appearance on our globe. Curiously enough, when it is a question of atomic structure, or of the nature of the electron, positron, proton, neutron, and other elementary particles, the scientist does not hesitate to confess his ignorance. The fact that these particles are, for the moment, no longer considered even as material entities, but as waves of probability, does not trouble him. He does not pretend to know or to understand. He only pretends to seek. That is the scientific attitude.

But as soon as we pass into the domain of life, this same physicist, who is imbued with modesty concerning the things he does know, is full of assurance and pride concerning the things he does not know. His purely sentimental convictions smother his critical sense. Faith kills good faith. In this he follows the directives of a small number of biologists whose important studies have probably prevented them from thinking. When a man is free and has no ambition except to try and understand the sequence of natural phenomena, it is much more honest to admit: I do not know.

I hope the reader will forgive me for not extending this criticism of the exclusive application of statistical laws, and of the second principle of thermodynamics, to living beings. I think I have shown that the success of such an attempt beyond the stage of the amoebae is—I will not say impossible, as the calculus of probabilities forbids the use of this word, but—at least highly improbable.

I would like to summarize the two most current attitudes on the subject of the role of chance, and on the significance of the words "laws of chance."

1st. The tolerant attitude, which we can actually consider as orthodox, according to the best authors (Bertrand,

Poincaré, Borel). We shall quote Poincaré's definition: [16]
"The expression 'laws of chance' does not necessarily signify absence of laws, but laws having such complex results
that their detailed analysis escapes us entirely—we can
only grasp the general tendency resulting from a great
number of partial effects that to a degree compensate each
other." Borel,[17] on the other hand, says: "The characteristic of phenomena that we call fortuitous, or due to
chance, is that they depend upon causes that are too complex to enable us to know and study them all."

This point of view therefore consists in blaming the in-
firmities of our senses and of our intelligence, and in
making them responsible for the necessity in which we
found ourselves of resorting to the calculus of probabilities.
There are numerous laws that escape us, but this has no
importance as, on our scale of observation, everything
occurs as if these laws did not exist, and as if chance alone
were the primordial factor.

Now, we can ask whether these elementary laws that
escape us are themselves laws of chance or, on the contrary, whether they express a pre-established order. It
must be one of two things: either, following the opinion
of Poincaré and Borel, individual laws exist which would
explain many things but relegate the laws of chance to
the rank of artificial interpretations, only valid on our
scale of observation and totally incapable of explaining
the evolution of the universe; or else—and this is the
second, the intransigent attitude—the laws of chance are
the only ones that count on every scale of observation.
Philosophically, this point of view is in accord with the
monist theory. I may have misinterpreted Poincaré and

[16] Poincaré, *Science et Méthode.*
[17] Borel, *Le Hasard.*

Borel, and, in speaking of "laws having such complex results that their detailed analysis escapes us" and "of too complex causes," these two authors may have meant statistical laws that are perhaps different but that express results due to chance alone. The birth of the new statistics, those of Bose-Einstein, or "photon statistics" as Guye calls them—which were unknown to Poincaré—and those of Pauli-Fermi which appeared after the publication of Borel's book, gives a certain likelihood to this hypothesis.

The preceding lines enable us to grasp clearly the two different ways of considering the laws of nature, or rather, the rules by which man can explain the sequence and foresee the appearance of natural phenomena.

The first way consists in admitting the existence of non-statistical laws that govern elementary particles and atoms individually. Their effects are so complex that "their analysis escapes us." They manifest themselves, on our scale of observation, by phenomena that we are unable to understand individually. This forces us to employ the calculus of probabilities, based on the hypothesis that all configurations, or all velocities, are equally probable.

The second way refuses definitely to admit the existence of phenomena obeying other laws than those of chance, on any scale of observation. This point of view seems to me to represent the creed of the materialists, or pure mechanists.

In the first case, considering that the macroscopic statistical laws are based on an incoordination between elements, we must admit that, if each particle is subject to a rigorous determinism, this determinism is peculiar to it and totally independent of the determinism governing the other particles. No interaction is possible, or rather, every interaction is indeterminate. The determination above the corpuscular scale is replaced by a statistical determination of another nature, the precision of which rests on the qualities and faults of the detector: Man. The problem of the harmony of the world remains whole and entirely subjective.

It is not certain that this point of view expresses the opinion of Henri Poincaré, if we are to judge by certain of his writings, and especially by the following sentence: "People ask the gods to prove their existence by miracles, but the eternal wonder is that miracles do not occur all the time. That is why the world is divine, that is why it is harmonious. If it were ruled by whim, what proof would we have that it was not ruled by chance?"

We shall not dwell further on this first opinion, which comes to the conclusion that a combination of the old and new determinism is necessary, without bringing any additional precisions. We shall only insist on the second more homogeneous opinion, which should unite the suffrage of a great number of scientists who are more or less heirs of the encyclopedists, positivists, and rationalists. We shall try to see if it enables us to dispense with unverifiable hypotheses.

It is evident that the determinism of Laplace has lost a great deal of significance since we have established our actual inability to fill the gaps that separate the properties of the constitutive elements from those of the whole (electrons-atoms, atoms-molecules, molecules-life, life-thought) and to link them together by causality. Indeed, a precise prediction of the velocity and position of all "the lightest atoms of the universe," even were it possible—and we know it is not—would not enable us to predict the phenomena we observe. We would find ourselves faced by systems of equations devoid of material significance, and would be as ignorant as when we were confronted by hieroglyphics, before the discovery of Champollion; as disarmed as the archeologist who seeks to evoke the living expression of a skull torn from its sepulchre. It is not absurd, moreover, to think that Laplace conceived the combination of individual determinisms and their fusion into a mass determinism. But then, if we admit evolution and progress, this brings us back to an absolute initial cause and to an unacceptable finalism. If we do not admit evolution and progress, it leads us to the total negation of an order and harmony, which, nevertheless, *it was determined we should conceive and project,* thanks to a consciousness and an intelligence that are determined though fortuitous, in an inevitable but meaningless universe. This is all rather contradictory and unconvincing.

In the first part of this study on the law of large numbers, we admitted the existence of atoms and molecules, and we showed that certain difficulties arise when we try to explain the appearance of a protein molecule and a living cell by the calculus of probabilities alone and without outside help. In other words, let us imagine a scientist who is a perfect mathematician and physicist, but totally ignorant of biological chemistry and biology. It would probably be easy for him to prove that molecules, such as proteins or enzymes, cannot exist and that life is inconceivable. Unfortunately, we know that there are proteins and that life, as well as thought, are unquestionable phenomena.

If this ideal scientist is endowed with imagination and faith in his science, he will not be at a loss to find a hypothesis that explains everything. This hypothesis will seem more plausible to him than any other, inasmuch as he proposed it and because the rules of the game require the problem to be solved with a limited number of elements, without calling on Maxwell's demon, or an extramaterial cause, or finalism. He will revolt against easy solutions, which consist in inventing a *primum movens,* an unknown force, which resolves all difficulties. In this he will not be wrong, but he will be obliged to resort to rather disconcerting and inconceivably complicated concepts: concepts that cannot be visualized by means of current mechanical models, and whose reality is purely mathematical and not directly controllable. Between two unverifiable hypotheses, one explaining everything unscientifically and the other explaining nothing, some scientists do not hesitate.

However, a number of the most eminent ones, even though they had the same faith in the supremacy of the human brain, did not think it necessary to adopt such an absolute philosophy. It is true that many of them were unacquainted with the prodigious development of the calculus of probabilities, the astonishing interpretation of the second principle of thermodynamics, and the new ideas concerning the electron. But I doubt if their opinion would have been modified by this knowledge, for they saw things differently, and their outstanding intelligence perceived a harmonious evolution which, to them, presented the main problem, and which the calculus of probabilities, notwithstanding its true beauty, cannot touch.[18]

[18] I cannot refrain from mentioning the beginning of the paragraph out of Borel's book which I quoted in Chapter I: ". . . The real inspiration of this splendid epic, the conquest of the world by man, is the faith in human reason, the conviction that the world is not ruled by blind gods or laws of chance, but by rational laws."

* * *

Thus, before the formation of atoms and molecules, which obey only statistical laws, as well as subsequently and in the most distant future, the elements that constitute them—electrons and protons—were, are, and will be, equally ruled by statistical laws. We have seen that the precision of these laws—which often exceeds all possibility of human control—depends on the number of these elements and on the perfect disorder of all their movements. This "perfect disorder" is absolutely necessary for the application of the calculus of probabilities. This is what is expressed in the last part of the sentence we used above to define probability: ". . . all possible cases being equally probable."

It is clear—and we have already insisted on this point— that if a certain number of the particles considered were endowed with special properties capable of affecting the phenomenon observed, they could, under certain conditions, facilitate the appearance of systematic fluctuations, which might affect the laws of chance. For all possible cases to be equally probable, it is necessary that all elements, placed in identical conditions, should, *on an average,* react identically, that is, there must not be any systematic deviation in one direction or another. Statistical laws, in conformity to this hypothesis, are found to apply in the realm of subatomic corpuscles. Curiously enough, however, it has been also discovered that other statistics have to be employed.

In the case of molecules or particles of matter, we have seen that one can, and should, apply the methods of combinatorial analysis. The number of "probable cases" is equal to that of possible "permutations." The same method is used for the calculus of probabilities relative to games of chance (heads or tails, dice, cards, etc.). These simple statistics can be called "macroscopic" and are schematized in the following manner (the diagrams below are borrowed from Guye):

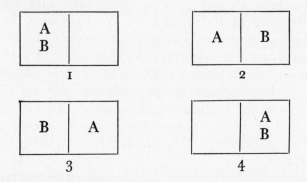

If we try to see how two particles, A and B, can be distributed in two compartments, we shall have the four possibilities shown above.

This distribution implies that the second combination is different from the third and that A is not identical to B. If these two elements were identical, they would be interchangeable, and 2 would be equivalent to 3. We are, therefore, led to attribute to A an appearance of *individuality*, different from that of B. If each of the four configurations is equally probable, the probability for the appearance of each one will be ¼ or 0.25.

Those are the Gibbs-Boltzmann statistics, which, as we have seen, give remarkable results on our scale of observation.

But when we try to apply these statistics of particles to electromagnetic radiation (photons), they lead us, with the principle of equipartition of energy, to Wien's radiation law, which we know is contradicted by experiment.

It is, therefore, necessary to employ other statistics,

known as the Bose-Einstein statistics, which differ from the preceding ones by the suppression of the personality of A and B. A no more differs from B than does one ball from another in ball bearings. As 2 and 3 are identical, only three repartitions are possible:

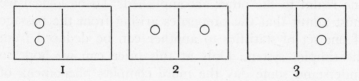

| I | 2 | 3 |

The elements, thus classed, are supposed to be two "molecular energies" and no longer two objects.

Each of these configurations has a probability of ⅓ or 0.3333 (instead of ¼). It is known that, strictly speaking, the individuality of A and B is not real and that A is in fact equivalent to B. Nevertheless, in certain cases, we must momentarily act as if this were not so. The reason for this is not clear.

The Pauli-Fermi statistics (statistics of electronic energies) go one step farther, and only admit the possibility of a single repartition, as in the following diagram:

The difference between this conception and macroscopic statistics is obvious.[19]

But, if this is the basis of the statistics that apply to electrons, how is it that more and more complex statistics appear successively?

[19] "A cell of the phase-space inside of an atom can only contain one electron, or no electron." Pauli's Exclusion Principle leads to this: two electrons can never occupy the same orbit.

How is it that the individuality of an atom, or of a molecule, appears all of a sudden out of void, or rather, out of chaos? I now consider the question from the point of view of specific properties and no longer from the point of view of calculation. How is the transition from one realm to the other accomplished? To be logical we must admit that the properties arising from the passage of one set of statistics to another can be deduced from the simpler system. Only at this price can we hope to understand some day the more complex phenomena of life and thought. According to our rationalistic and mechanistic faith, we have no right to call in outside help, namely, help that cannot be put into equations. We must therefore seek in Pauli-Fermi's mathematical conceptions and in Schrödinger's probability waves the elements of that which will eventually become a newborn child—the genius of a Lavoisier or of a Pasteur.

The task is overwhelming, but we lack neither courage nor optimism. The following passage by Langevin is proof of this: ". . . Individual character in physics, as in biology, is a character that results from the complexity of structure. . . . The individual, capable of being isolated and recognized, only appears at a certain degree of complexity. In order to individualize, to follow and to recognize an object, we must be able to distinguish the minimum of characters required to give an experimental meaning to personality. It seems to me that the concept of personality has no clearly defined inferior limit, and stands out more and more clearly as the structure becomes more complicated." [20]

No one will deny the logic of these lines. One can, at

[20] P. Langevin, *La Notion de Corpuscule et d'Atome*, Hermann and Cie, Paris, 1934.

most, regret the absence of detail concerning precisely the manner in which the individual character suddenly appears out of one certain complexity of structure, and not out of another. The author passes over in silence the fact that the complexity in question is not an indifferent kind of complexity, but is organized and harmoniously coordinated. *It is from the coordination of complexity that the properties of a cell are born and not from the chaotic complexity which characterizes a gas mixture.*[21]

The explanations given by Langevin may appease his intellectual curiosity, but I doubt whether they will satisfy everybody. These statements are evident *a posteriori* and remind us of Molière's celebrated "explanation" of the soporific properties of the poppy: "Quia est in ipso virtus dormitiva." [22] We are slightly surprised that Langevin adopted an attitude closely related to that of the partisans of the Emergence theory. Indeed, this way of conceiving the birth of one, or several, new properties that cannot be foreseen from the qualities of the constitutive elements may already be found in Herbert Spencer, who thus "explains" the appearance of consciousness. It has been developed in our day under the name of Theory of Emergent Evolution, or Theory of Emergence. Following this theory, life and thought are properties that emerge from certain material aggregates. A complete knowledge of their constituents would not enable us to predict that life and thought necessarily result from their combination or conjunction. Logically, this must apply to the properties of atoms and molecules constituted by electrons and protons. Here again we obviously have a form of subjectivism.

[21] See: Ch. Eug. Guye on this subject: *Les Fontières de la Physique et de la Biologie.*
[22] "Because it contains a soporific quality."

Certain scientists simply say that the reason we cannot foresee new properties lies in our incomplete knowledge of the constitutive elements. But the Emergence theory goes one step farther and affirms that the properties of water are not implicitly contained in those of oxygen and hydrogen. Neither can the properties of life be inferred even from a complete knowledge of the proteins or their constituent atoms.

It is easy to see how much this theory simplifies matters. It is henceforth useless to take the trouble to understand the disquieting transitions we mentioned above: the fundamental "scale problems." We shall never be able to solve them, according to this theory, no matter how great our science is. In other words, we are brought back to absolute beginnings, which scientists in general violently dislike. Moreover, if we admit the principle of absolute beginnings, we can oppose only purely sentimental and aesthetic objections, not arguments, to Genesis and to the explanations given by religion.

The grave weakness of this hypothesis lies in the fact that we cannot prove it to be correct, but that we can conceive the possibility of proving it to be false. Indeed, we cannot demonstrate that it will be impossible to deduce the properties of water from those of hydrogen and oxygen when our knowledge of these two atoms will be increased. We cannot tell. And if this were some day possible, the theory of Emergence would be disproved and would join the old-fashioned theory of Materialism, which tried to explain thought by the movements of little hard elastic balls in the brain. The theory of Emergence is not a working hypothesis. It is not even scientific.

In short, we see that the main problem does not begin with the formation of a protein molecule—which will be solved some day [23]—nor with the creation of a cell, but much farther back, with the creation of an atom and a single molecule. At present, in spite of the immense number of problems solved, the questions that remain unanswered seem to increase day by day. This is primarily due to the tremendous progress in wave mechanics, where every discovery seems to reveal our ignorance a little more.

Let us not forget that the Schrödinger waves, in general, move in a polydimensional space, and do not transport energy, but probabilities of distribution of energy; and finally that the intra-atomic phenomena, to which they give birth, are practically independent of temperature, in opposition to atomic, molecular, and biological phenomena, which are subject to laws based on the macroscopic statistics of Gibbs-Boltzmann. The bridge between the two classes of phenomena will have to be established first of all, and thermodynamics linked to wave mechanics. We have seen (p. 109) that up till now all efforts in this direction have failed.

* * *

The laws of chance have rendered and will continue to render tremendous services to science. We cannot conceive of doing without them. In most cases they correspond to a necessity; but there are other cases where they cannot apply—problems of species, for instance, which cannot be neglected.

To believe that biological phenomena in general and the evolution of organized beings in particular can be explained by the same principles, the same calculations,

[23] This does not mean that the day a protein molecule will have been synthesized, we will have the faintest idea of the manner in which the first albumin molecule was formed at the time of the appearance of life on earth.

as those used to estimate the number of houses that will burn, or the pressure of a gas in a vessel, is an act of faith. The examples of insurances, or of kinetic theory, though they may be appealing, are really too simple and can satisfy only an indolent mind. Indeed, the problems of life are manifold and more intricate than those of the calculation of premiums and stockholders' dividends. Extrapolation is not legitimate and we find ourselves precisely in the case we mentioned at the end of the second chapter.

In the realm of human psychology, Borel implicitly voiced this criticism in the following wise observation: "Neither common sense, nor calculations, can insure us against misfortune, and it will always be a meager consolation for an individual to think that the probability of misfortune was slight, when he is the one to suffer from it."

All that we can hope to learn from a calculation of insurances is a percentage—of fire, accident, or death—based on experience and on the statistics for a few preceding years. All that can be deduced from the calculus of probabilities is a rate of probability, and its weak point consists in the fact that all events must be considered as equally probable. When the figures are in accord with the experiment, we conclude that they were, in fact, equally probable. But even for simple phenomena of the inorganic universe this is not certain. The scale of observation again comes into play as numerical verifications can be made only with inadequate precision, and during much too short a period of time—a few years for instance. If the control could last for millions of years, it would be more convincing. The evolution of human beings is extremely slow compared to the evolution of conditions that apply to insurance statistics. The importance of the factor Time must not be underestimated.

Furthermore, when we consider living beings, it becomes impossible to neglect the individual: physiologically, for the simpler organisms, physiologically and psychologically, for man. Evolution depends on a large number of factors and we are far from knowing the complete mechanism. Each of the great theories of evolution—that of Lamarck (adaptation), of Darwin (natural selection by the survival of the fittest), of de Vries (sudden mutations)— probably contains a part of the truth. A combination of the three gives us an approximate idea of evolution as a whole that is not quite correct but that satisfies the mind.

The individual plays a fundamental part in this whole. It is always one individual, or a small number as compared to the mass, who steers evolution in a certain direction. *Fluctuations are not sufficient to explain facts qualitatively. They only enable us to conceive that they are not impossible quantitatively.*

Accordingly, we can only conclude once more that macroscopic statistical laws (Gibbs-Boltzmann statistics) are no longer valid in the realm of organized beings. We must seek something else. This statement may hurt the convictions of a certain number of scientists: the idea that the same principles and the same laws cannot apply to two series of phenomena is inadmissible, for they refuse to admit that there is a fundamental difference between the two. Nature is One, except for the partisans of Emergence. We cannot conceive a duality of laws without turning toward an undesirable form of dualism. It is possible that this duality only expresses, once again, the infirmity of our brains, just as it is possible that unity is a myth. The rational elements that we possess are not sufficient to enable us to make a truly scientific affirmation. We are forced to introduce into our judgments sentimental elements that resemble those we mentioned when speaking of the disagreement between Einstein and Eddington (note, p. 30).

As we are not able to reach to the very essence of things, we tend to suppress this sentimental element that cannot be measured. We have already said that science can only take quantity into account, whereas, psychologically, man only perceives quality. This creates grave difficulties and it is hard to see how they can be solved. Man may never succeed in doing so, but this would not in itself constitute a proof that the unity of nature does not exist. It would only indicate that either we are incapable of perceiving and of explaining certain transitions, or that "absolute beginnings" really exist, or, at any rate, phenomena that we are incapable of interpreting otherwise.

At present it does not seem possible, on the sole basis of the calculus of probabilities, to do without the hypothesis of an "anti-chance." So far, the opponents of this thesis have given us no scientific proofs, only sentimental arguments, in favor of their point of view. They will not be astonished if a certain number of scientists, who value scientific methods more than they do, reserve their judgment until these proofs are given, even though they respect, whenever possible, a faith that may be debatable but is nevertheless sincere.

It is an undeniable fact that, as we advance in the study of nature, we observe the appearance of beings who are more and more independent, until at the top of the ladder we finally find man, with his weaknesses and his grandeur, man who not only thinks and believes, *but for whom it is important that what he believes should be true.*

CERTAIN SCIENTIFIC THEORIES

Arguments

Man has always sought to explain the origin of life. For a long time scientists accumulated facts but it took a Newton, a Kepler, a Cuvier, a Lamarck to coordinate these facts and transform them into theories.

EVOLUTION has imposed itself as a concept in spite of the fact that many links are still missing. The true key of the enigma of evolution may never be found.

DETERMINISM, as defined by Laplace, is no longer valid since Heisenberg's investigations.

FINALISM offers a coordinating hypothesis that presupposes a distant goal but admits different methods for the attainment of this goal. The calculus of probability can be applied to it, it is not in contradiction with the concept of entropy. To understand it we must observe it from a distance as if appreciating the beauty of a cathedral.

It is highly probable that the subjective scientific relations we establish are only an echo of parallel relations in the objective universe. However, as we shall never be able to perceive this universe without the intermediary of our senses, this problem is beyond the limits of science.

6

CERTAIN SCIENTIFIC THEORIES

EVOLUTION · DETERMINISM · HEISENBERG'S
PRINCIPLE · FINALISM

THE "explanation" of plants, animals, and man has at all times preoccupied men. Creation by an all-powerful God was the first, most simple and direct solution to this problem. It is found in all religions under different aspects.

This solution has the advantage of being uncomplicated. But for many people who are endowed with the exacerbated curiosity that successively engendered philosophers, alchemists, and scientists, it has the disadvantage of stating the problem without solving it. Indeed, how can we refrain from being interested in the method by which God created life from inert matter? How can we avoid being puzzled by the immense number of different species? How can we help being astonished by the profound differences that exist between primitive invertebrates and dinosaurs, between the latter and modern mammals, between the pterodactyl or the archaeopterix and birds, between animals in general and man, and how can we keep from discerning relationships and similarities between species that impose the idea of evolution?

It was natural, therefore, that man should not deem

himself thoroughly satisfied and that he should try to clarify certain details. The first effort in this direction consisted in accumulating facts. For a long time naturalists observed, described, and piled up document on document. The perusal of works, such as those of Buffon and his collaborators, cannot fail to impress us by their incomparable amplitude. But a collection of descriptions does not constitute a scientific work. A catalogue does not require imagination, and the archivist of facts, even if he is indispensable, does not contribute to the progress of our knowledge of the universe.

The movements of the planets, the eclipses of the sun and of the moon had been scrupulously described for a long time—eclipses were calculated at the time of the Chaldeans—but a Newton and a Kepler were needed to coordinate these facts and to elucidate phenomena that had remained mysterious.

In the same way, Cuvier and Lamarck were needed to discover the guiding thread in the animal world. Their genius revealed the first unsuspected links, which in time were transformed into the theory of evolution.

Lamarck's transformism, Darwin's evolutionism, developed and embellished by Spencer and Haeckel, and the de Vries theory of mutations each had their passionate defenders. The obscure problems of heredity were tackled, and often clarified, by Mendel, Weissmann and, recently, by Morgan and Spemann. But there is still no complete and entirely satisfactory theory of evolution.

Professor Maurice Caullery, an eminent specialist on the question, recently outlined the actual state of the problem and I cannot do better than to quote the following passage: [1] "Another difficulty, which must not be ignored

[1] *Science,* 1938.

nor minimized, concerns the realization of evolution in time. Geological and physical data (in particular, facts revealed by radioactivity), enable us to estimate the duration of the fossiliferous periods as being of the order of a billion years. We are far from the 6000 years of Genesis. But the organisms dating from the remotest ages hardly differ from those of today. Charles D. Walcott very ably studied marvelously preserved fossils of various groups, belonging to the Cambrian period, which he found in the Rocky Mountains. Without doubt, the forms are different from those of today, but they enter into the frame of actual groups, and even their organization does not differ in any way from that of modern species. The cells and the activities of these organisms must be considered as identical to those that exist nowadays. Bashford Dean was able to study the histology of the kidneys in the Silurian selachian fishes. It is the same as that of the kidneys belonging to selachians in our seas. The formation of organized nature as a whole, and even in detail, therefore dates back beyond a billion years and beyond all accessible geological periods. On the other hand Pasteur's assertion still holds. Nothing indicates a spontaneous generation, nothing allows us to postulate independent and successive formations, *ex nihilo,* of series of organisms during the geological periods. On the contrary, the complete uniformity of the constitution of animals and vegetables in itself implies a common origin. No matter how far back we look, we do not see life beginning, but continuing. We must admit that life began, but its origin remains entirely mysterious.

"The general fact that paleontology only shows us a few transitional forms, and still fewer really primitive forms, is also very disturbing. As we have already reminded

the reader, we know only an infinitesimal number of beings which have existed, but we do not grasp the origin
of any group. Any progress made usually consists in the
discovery that each one of the groups is much older than
we had previously thought, and when they manifest themselves at a determined epoch they are, from the beginning, represented by very diversified and specialized forms.
We totally ignore how and when the primitive diversification took place.

"Mammals undeniably represent one of the high peaks
of evolution and their diversification occurred only recently, in the tertiary epoch, that is to say, in the last 20
or 30 million years. The tertiary period is really the era
of mammals: at this epoch we actually witness the evolution of different families. But all the fundamental
groups appear abruptly at the beginning of the Eocene
period. This implies a very long and manifold previous
evolution during the secondary period, or even earlier.
For the moment we only have traces of it, which are as
isolated as they are insignificant. It is, nevertheless, true
that the history of the tertiary mammals in itself gives a
striking verification of evolution. No other group supplies
us with comparable facts.

"In brief, evolution remains an impressive concept, the
only one capable of explaining living nature rationally
and, on the whole, it imposes itself as a fact. But its
mechanism still escapes us and even its history is only
known in fragments that are insignificant in comparison
to reality.

"Let us, therefore, be proud that our intelligence has
been able to construct on such fragile bases the syntheses
that are at our disposal and that are dominated by the
names of Lamarck, Geoffroy Saint-Hilaire, Lyell, Dar-

win, Wallace, Weismann, de Vries, Morgan, etc. But let us remain modest. So far, nature has only given up a minute part of her secrets, and those that are the true key of the enigma run a great chance of remaining inaccessible for a long time to come, if not forever."

These lines, which brilliantly sum up the actual state of the question, deserve to be meditated. They show how far the question has progressed since 1900. As documents deserving of credit accumulated, the quasi-absolute confidence in human theories weakened. The difficulties today, far from lessening, have increased. The origin of life remains a mystery, inferior organisms do not appear to evolve; regressions are even observed. Only the mammals, the newcomers—what are 20 or 30 million years compared to a thousand million?—give us a proof of evolution. They seem to appear "abruptly" at the beginning of the Eocene period. How are they linked to reptiles, and the latter to fish and to invertebrates? We have no idea.

Several mechanisms have been called upon to explain the processes of evolution, and all of them can very well have played a part. It seems, however, that not enough attention has been paid up till now to a factor that may have to be taken into consideration: namely, immunity.

Indeed, it is probable that without immunity all the animal species, and certainly the most evolved, the human species, would have long since disappeared from the surface of the globe. We have a fairly recent example in a colony of convicts who were established, for some kind of exploitation, in the north of Siberia. The children were born and grew up in a rigorously cold, dry climate, completely isolated from civilization and sheltered from all infectious diseases. When, for some reason or other, the whole colony was transported to the south, near a village adjoining the railroad, most of the children died as a result of different infections that they immediately contracted. I have myself witnessed a similar, though less striking, case in an out-of-the-way corner of Arizona in 1922.[2] I was with an army doctor, who was in charge of the health administration of the Indian Reservation, and we visited a small pueblo that had not been in constant contact with the whites. (A few such places still exist in Arizona, Utah, and in the southern part of Nevada.) The doctor told me that at the end of World War I the government had sent some engineers to study an irrigation project. In addition, the Indians had begun to have more frequent contacts with the whites at the nearest trading post. In less than a year, and in spite of the fact that there were only about twenty whites, none of whom apparently had tuberculosis, an epidemic of that disease broke out and, according to the doctor, killed off more than half the children and young people, leaving the others in a critical condition. The tuberculosis manifested itself in a rare form, known by the name of miliary tuberculosis.[3] Examples could be multiplied.

The most necessary form of adaptation is, therefore, the adaptation to microbic infections. The theory of adaptation takes into account only the adaptation to external conditions: temperature, light, darkness, pressure, food, etc. Chemical adaptation, with perhaps the exception of food, is not considered. Yet it seems that this phenomenon, on a molecular scale, is fundamentally important. Though the mechanism involved is still very mysterious, we know positively nowadays (as a consequence of the work of

[2] In the vicinity of Chinlee, near the Cañon de Chelly, in the Navajo Reservation.

[3] Because of the myriads of minute superficial abscesses, no bigger than a millet seed.

Landsteiner, Avery, Heidelberger, Goebel, etc.), that immunity is a phenomenon of an essentially chemical nature. But we still do not understand how the fact of injecting any type of toxic or non-toxic protein can, within two weeks, start the fabrication in the organism of a chemical compound (antibody) which is specifically endowed with the property of neutralizing the action of the first (antigen).

It makes no difference what antigenic substance is injected, nor how unlikely its introduction into the organism may be (egg albumin, castor oil, proteins combined with sugars, sodium tartrates, etc.), which eliminates hereditary "memory," the organism will oppose a strictly specific molecule, incapable of reacting to any other antigen.[4] The antibody and the antigen are adapted to each other like a safety lock and key.

This manifestation in a living being of a defense phenomenon, on a molecular scale, is altogether remarkable and is expressed, on the scale of the individual, by a faculty of adaptation that must have played an important part in the development and selection of the species.

It is interesting to note that this process is a possible application of Le Châtelier's "Law of moderation," or of "counter-action,"[5] which would thus intervene as a determining factor not only in the defense of living organisms, *but in evolution in general.* This idea could only acquire convincing strength, and a certain precision, if the

---

[4] Lecomte du Noüy, *Biological Time,* Macmillan, New York, 1937, pp. 40 to 48.

[5] This law is expressed in the following manner: when a physico-chemical system is in stable equilibrium the variation of one of the factors, on which this equilibrium depends, has the effect of producing a modification which precisely tends to oppose the variation of this factor. (See Guye, *Les Frontières de la Physique et de la Biologie.*)

scale of the problem could be changed, that is to say, if this process of adaptation could be linked to a phenomenon clearly dependent on the statistical laws of physico-chemistry. As we have just seen, this is now possible, thanks to modern discoveries in the field of immunity.

Nevertheless, this observation raises an immediate objection. Le Châtelier's law can only be applied to "stable equilibria." Therefore, it is not general, and a living organism cannot be considered as a stable equilibrium in a physico-chemical sense. Yet the stability of life corresponds to a reality. It is a dynamic stability which evokes that of a flowing stream or of a burning candle. On the other hand, we have seen that the problem could be reduced to chemical phenomena in the organism; and we are, apparently, authorized to consider the internal medium of a living being as a chemical system, with a great character of stability. We know, indeed, that the body fluids react rigorously against all causes tending to introduce a variation in the constancy of the internal medium. The pH (which measures the alkalinity or acidity of serum, protoplasm, and body fluids) and interfacial tension, for example, are maintained at a mean value, which only shows very feeble oscillations, even when one tries artificially to destroy the equilibrium by means of well-known "buffer" mechanisms.[6]

We cannot, therefore, speak of a stable equilibrium on the "individual" scale. But on the molecular scale of the body fluids, of blood serum, for example, it seems that we are authorized to do so. Consequently, it may be admitted that the "law of moderation" in its actual form, or *in a more general form,* can be hypothetically regarded as the

[6] Lecomte du Noüy: *Surface Equilibria of Colloids.* Chemical Catalog Co. (Reinhold Publishing Corp.), New York, 1926.

expression of one of the basic factors of adaptation, considered as a process of evolution.

* * *

The books published in the last twenty years on the theory of relativity have been so numerous and excellent that I will not attempt to speak of it. I have not the audacity to think that I could do better, nor even the illusion that I could do as well.

This prodigious effort of the human brain, which for the first time has established a correlation between the measurement of time and that of space, which for the first time has given us a coherent interpretation (though not explanation) of the force of gravitation, and which has shown the uselessness of the embarrassing hypothesis of ether,[7] has since the beginning of the 20th century upset all science and steered it into a definitely new path from which it has not deviated. Like a human being, the theory of relativity has developed, enriched, and modified itself in the course of years. It will still evolve. Far from decreasing its value, these successive transformations have on the contrary increased it. Today a physicist "thinks in relativity." Yet we must not forget the relativity of relativity itself, nor lose sight of the fact that the only goal of similar theories is to throw slender gangways between isles of knowledge in an ocean of ignorance.

A voluminous literature has been published on the subject. There are pamphlets and ponderous volumes that were written for every kind of public, at all stages of culture. Einstein himself did not hesitate to publish a small book of popularization, which was rather severely criticized

[7] To which certain authors at present have a tendency to return, under a different form.

by some people, because the examples chosen where sometimes in contradiction with the pure mathematical theory. This is the almost inevitable fate of books of popularization when they attempt to explain, without mathematical symbols, concepts that can hardly be expressed otherwise without losing their rigor and clearness.

The ideas of physicists on the material world tend to become more and more mathematical. "Mechanical models" are the only artifices that enable a non-mathematician to conceive the physical significance of a theory. But they are not without danger, and Louis de Broglie, the genial inventor of "wave mechanics" that revolutionized physics, formally warns the scientist against this danger. The mathematical concepts of the elementary "corpuscles" —which are no longer material particles—simply express the probability for an electron, for instance, to be at a certain point or, more exactly, the probability for the properties, which we attribute to this electron, to be found at this place. Every particle in motion is accompanied by an associated wave. But, as Maurice de Broglie, his brother, explains, these new waves intervene more as an artifice of calculation than as a new physical phenomenon.

It is now possible, by means of the Louis de Broglie and Schrödinger equations, to describe and foresee the relations between phenomena with much greater precision and logic. This is the goal of science. But it is impossible to visualize the elements employed. Only on a certain scale do mechanical models begin to have a meaning and, even then, they must only be used with extreme caution.

We shall now rapidly examine a theory that had an immense philosophical success—determinism—after which we shall dwell briefly on the doctrine of finalism. There is, evidently, no relation between these two theories and the theory of relativity: the first two are more a philosophical attitude than a working tool. The word "theory," moreover, is often employed with different meanings. It sometimes signifies "a group of rules and rigorous mathematical considerations"—the theory of numbers, the theory of steam or electromagnetic engines—and it sometimes signifies "hypothesis"—kinetic theory of gases, Laplace theory, Einstein theory.

We shall take the word in this latter sense. A theory can then be compared to a case that is built to hold a very complicated scientific instrument. All the different parts of the instrument must fit into the case without effort. But it never pretends to be part of the instrument itself.

Laplace [8] defined determinism in the following manner: "We ought then to regard the present state of the universe as the effect of its antecedent state and as the cause of the state that is to follow. An intelligence that, for a given instant, could know all the forces that animate nature and the respective positions of the entities composing it, and furthermore was vast enough to submit these data to analysis, would include in one and the same formula the movements of the largest bodies in the universe and those of the lightest atoms. Nothing would be uncertain for him; the future as well as the past would be present to his eyes. The human mind, by the perfection it has been able to give to astronomy, offers a faint outline of such an intelligence. All efforts in the search for truth tend to approach, without limit, the intelligence we have just imagined."

One of two things: either this definition is valid or it is

[8] Laplace, *Essai Philosophique sur les Probabilités*, 1814.

not valid. I naturally take the point of view of the convinced determinist, according to the classical definition. Though I have read criticisms of the statistical theory of determinism (which was outlined in a preceding chapter), I have never succeeded, in spite of repeated efforts, in finding another definition of determinism, though in the articles and books devoted to its study or defense I came across restrictions that remove all value from Laplace's definition. The following sentence, for instance: "Determination is built up gradually, as events take place. That is all one can say." [9] I may be wrong, but it seems to me that, if determination is built up gradually as events take place, it shows that there is no determination, in Laplace's meaning of the word.

I do not intend to criticize one theory in favor of another, as is frequently done. A writer usually reveals his true convictions at one moment or another no matter how clever he is, and thus destroys the value of his arguments. I am, therefore, compelled to admit that Laplace's definition expresses the orthodox credo of the 100 per cent determinist, and I will try to deduce its logical consequences.

First of all, I do not think that anyone, nowadays, denies the existence of a certain determinism that expresses the continuity of nature—the determinism I spoke of on page 32—namely, macroscopic determinism on our scale of observation. This determinism constitutes the very foundation of our human science; and this foundation is so solid and so necessary that its extrapolation to all phenomena of the universe, including subatomic phenomena, seemed logical and legitimate.

This determinism is not a theory. It is a statement *a*

[9] Matisse, *L'Arrangement de l'Univers par l'Esprit,* p. 165, Alcan, 1938.

posteriori. It has no place in Laplace's definition, or more exactly, Laplace would never have taken the trouble to write his definition if he had only had in mind the description of this law of evident and elementary causality.

The problem of knowing whether this order of succession, this sequence, is merely subjective, or whether it corresponds to a similar sequence in external events that determine our sensations, is purely academic and without great interest. It is highly probable that the subjective relations we establish are only an echo of the relations existing in the objective universe, which our consciousness translates or interprets in its own way. As we shall never be able to perceive our universe without the intermediary of our senses, this problem is outside the limits of science. Let us imagine a sound camera locked up in a booth and projecting an opera on the screen. If we do not know the mechanism, we can suppose that the picture corresponds identically to what goes on in the booth, where actors sing the words we hear, while we see them by means of mirrors. By reasoning a little we can think that it is our retina and our brain that are responsible for the impression of continuity and motion, and that there is only a succession of pictures in the booth which each represent stable and motionless personages. If we could see the film itself, we would perceive that we were right. But we would be unable to understand where the music and the voices came from. We could not establish the relation between the thin, irregular strip that is the result of the photography of sound and the harmony that strikes our ears. Yet the sequence of sounds that constitutes the opera corresponds on the film to a succession of irregularities that are related to each other exactly as are the phenomena that, by the intermediary of our ears, culminate in our consciousness and gives us an impression of the human voice and of the orchestra. The example is crude but it enables us to grasp the idea of translation of which I spoke.

To discuss whether the universe is "causal" or "acausal" strikes me as a harmless but futile occupation. We shall not escape determinism, which forces us to think causally, as all our science and its laws prove.

There remains true determinism, the determinism of Laplace, which is only an extrapolation, as I stated above. Indeed, what does he say exactly? That a vast enough intelligence "would include in one and the same formula the movements of the largest bodies in the universe and those of the lightest atoms . . . the future as well as the past would be present to his eyes."

This is a rigid conception of the world: no event is independent, and all events are tied to each other and determined by each other. Not only are they linked at the actual moment but they are the inevitable consequence of past events and contain, potentially, all future events that will succeed each other during billions of years. The universe evolved in the only possible way; there was only one path for the earth to follow as soon as it had separated from the sun; the path that could already be foreseen—by a vast intelligence—at the time when the whole Milky Way was only a spiral nebula in a gaseous state.

The astronomer Delaunay used to say: "When I lift my arm I disturb the moon." Yes, but if he lifted his arm he could not prevent lifting it; therefore, he had to disturb the moon at that minute and the moon had to be disturbed. If he had not lifted his arm it would have been because it was predetermined that he should not lift it. But if the astronomer had hesitated to disturb the moon who can tell what influence the conflict would have had on his mind?

In fact, if he had hesitated, it would have been because his hesitation was predetermined; and so on.

We cannot object that such an insignificant act could not possibly influence the movements of the planets. The *idea* of exploiting the power of the tides on a large scale does not represent a measurable, nor even an appreciable, quantity of energy. But it is not absurd to think that men will decide to put this idea in practice, two or three centuries hence, if their reserves of oil and coal dwindle. In the course of the following centuries this would probably result in a decrease of the velocity of the rotation of the earth around its axis. The days would be longer and the movements of the moon might be influenced. And yet, from an energy standpoint, the effort involved in merely thinking the thought—of harnessing the tides to produce power—will have been billions of times weaker than that of lifting the arm. But what does it matter since they were both "determined"?

It is easy to see that, from a moral standpoint, this theory leads to a complete fatalism, though the attempt has been made to establish a difference between the two. If man does not have the certitude—or the hope—that an effort of will (therefore, a manifestation of his free will) can steer events in a more favorable or better direction, he will naturally fall into a kind of indifference that will result in Mohammedan fatalism. Personally, I cannot see the difference between "it was written" and "it was determined."

Clearly, there is a solution of continuity somewhere in our reasoning. On the one hand, we are forced to admit a causality that extends its manifestations far into our perceptible world. We understand a certain determinism on our scale of observation. But we instinctively hesitate—

perhaps wrongly so—when we fall into the realm of the "trigger causes" and of volition, which bring into play infinitesimal quantities of energy, momentarily inappreciable.

One wonders if this is not another scale "problem" like those encountered in the study of the analytical method. Now, when we consider that the first one-way threshold found—when we deal with the smallest elements, the electrons—is irrefutably demonstrated by the fact that wave mechanics, which enable us to interpret the subatomic phenomena, is not applicable to macroscopic phenomena —namely, phenomena that constitute our perceptible universe—we cannot avoid thinking that the solution of continuity, to which we alluded above, perhaps corresponds to this kind of break, or fault, in the continuity of our interpretation of the world by calculus.

On the one hand, we would have the concrete unities endowed with specific properties and with mass, which form the substratum of matter, atoms and molecules. On the other hand, we would have the constitutive "entities" of atoms, deprived of the material properties belonging to them, obeying other laws in a universe where the words "Time" and "Space" no longer possess the same meaning.

Now these fundamental elements, unknown to Laplace, must, according to the strict definition of determinism, be themselves subjected to the laws of causality. They are doubtless what Laplace meant by the "lightest atoms." If this is not the case, if the determinists take the word "atom" in a chemical sense, then determinism stops at atoms: it is a blind alley. But how can we admit that the qualities of the atoms are not determined by the qualities of the electrons, or by properties resulting from the mutual deportment of electrons and protons? These properties must be determined by something, or else we come up against an absolute beginning, without a preliminary cause, which the determinist cannot admit. (See p. 73.)

Causal relations must then exist between the atoms, considered as individuals, and the elementary particles, deprived of individuality, which constitute them. If this is not the case, integral determinism is not only shaken but non-existent, so to speak. If these relations exist they must, perforce, have their origin in the particles themselves, and their positions and movements must be strictly determined. Now we know that, apparently, this is not the case.

* * *

So many brilliant authors have written volumes on the important question of Heisenberg's principle of indeterminacy that we feel slightly embarrassed in broaching it. On the other hand, the few observations we wish to make are justified by the fact that they stem from motives different from those that inspired previous writers. Therefore, the angle from which these problems will be considered may possibly bring enough fresh elements to steer the thoughts of the informed reader into a new channel. If by chance this should be the case, our effort will not have been in vain.

Heisenberg demonstrated that we never possess more than half of the information necessary to predict the future action of an electron in an atomic orbit. Or, more exactly, if we come back to Laplace's statement, which speaks of "including in one and the same formula," we will say that *exactly half* the symbols will represent knowable quantities, and the other half unknowable quantities. It is not a question of a basic limitation due to our methods of measurement or to our senses; it is a basic limitation resting on the reciprocal interaction of observation and phenomenon.

We shall give a rough illustration of what is meant by the foregoing sentence. Let us invent a new game of billiards that must be played blindfolded, and where the balls in motion are localized by sound: they are hollow and contain a rattle. Supposing the game no longer consists in making a carom, but simply in knocking the ball with another held in the hand. We can admit that a trained player, with an instrument for localizing sound tied onto his head, could follow the movement of the ball and could aim and hit it. He is only absolutely sure of the position it occupies, and of the velocity that animated it, when the ball he sends hits it. The noise of the impact confirms the exactitude of his aim. But the impact itself has deviated the ball, which is no longer in the place where it was hit. He can, therefore, not know the actual position of the ball. In other words, the impact, which is indispensable to reveal the place of the ball, results in an immediate change of direction and velocity in the ball aimed at. Therefore, it is impossible for the player to verify the position and velocity of the ball he is aiming at experimentally as the experiment changes them both. The observation affects the phenomenon because the balls have an equivalent mass and velocities of the same order.

This comparison is extremely crude, it is even incorrect. But it enables one to understand, roughly, Heisenberg's phenomenon, which brings into play one photon (a quantum of light) and one electron. During this process of observation, the photon which has touched the electron has altered the velocity and position of the latter. The photon, which is diffracted by the electron, and which then proceeds to impress the retina (this is where the example is incorrect), does not give a precise indication of the velocity and place of the electron. In fact we know that the electron itself is no longer considered as a material point. One can only speak of "fogs" whose density, at any place, is proportional to the probability that the electron is at that place.

According to Heisenberg's theory, the precision with which we can ascertain the position of a particle increases to the detriment of the precision with which we can estimate its speed. If one of two paired symbols is known with certainty and accuracy, the other must be altogether unknown; but if one is partially known, the other may be partially known. The uncertainty of the quantity q, multiplied by the uncertainty of the paired quantity p, is of the order of magnitude of Planck's constant h.

Cases exist, even on our scale of observation, which show a certain relation to those considered by Heisenberg. For example, it is impossible to know the color of the emulsion of an undeveloped photographic plate in white light. Indeed, we know that this light chemically affects this emulsion, and we do not know if this reaction does not manifest itself by a coloration of the emulsion. In order to know if the plate, before exposure to light, is of a different color (pure white, for example), we would be obliged to illuminate it, which immediately affects it. Experimentally speaking, a virgin emulsion has no color.

If, then, we take the word determinism in the same sense as Laplace, we inevitably come to elements that are not determined in respect to us. To say that indeterminism ceases if we suppress the observer is to contradict Laplace's statement and to introduce an unverifiable hypothesis. The principle of uncertainty is, therefore, linked to the problem of determinism.

There is another way of conceiving determinism, which consists in saying that "determination is built up gradually as events take place." In addition to the fact that this way of thinking has nothing in common with that of Laplace, it does not seem to us competent to suppress the difficulty. For this would be the admission that a state of indetermination exists until a certain event suppresses it. If this event is not indetermined, it is determined, and we fall back on Laplace's statement. If it is indetermined, up to the moment of action (see definition above) we come back to Heisenberg's statement.

Thus the concept of rigid determinism, which was already shaken by the introduction of the calculus of probabilities as a method of interpretation, is defeated by Heisenberg's principle of uncertainty, or indeterminacy.[10]

Determinism must be rigid, total, and must conform to Laplace's dictum if it is to keep its philosophical value. Every attempt to make it more supple, such as the successive determination of consequent events, introduces a contradictory element of indeterminacy. We know that past events have been determined and could not have taken place in any other way; but they must have taken place before we can affirm that they were determined. In a word, *any event whatsoever introduces something new into the world that was not entirely contained in the past.*

The great practical superiority of the calculus of probabilities consists in the fact that it maintains with extreme rigor the notion of determinism on our scale of observation, that it enables correct scientific laws to be established and interprets fundamental principles of physical evolu-

[10] A recent and important book that goes farther than any other into the fundamental structure of the physical universe does not mention the existence of a scheme of strictly causal law. (P.A.M. Dirac, *The Principles of Quantum Mechanics,* Clarendon Press, Oxford). See also, Sir Arthur Eddington.

tion, such as Carnot's law, without imprisoning us in a steel coffin. We have seen that the law of large numbers does not succeed in giving us a plausible, or probable, explanation of the phenomenon of life, in spite of the flexibility derived from the possibility of fluctuations. Determinism does not even attack these problems, for it is not, and never has been, a constructive tool, and in no case can it explain any kind of evolution whatsoever. Like the calculus of probabilities, it only admits chance as the one driving force. But it only makes this chance intervene once, at the beginning of the universe, and everything that follows is the ineluctable consequence of this first throw of the dice. It is an essentially restful doctrine for a mind deprived of curiosity. The calculus of probabilities also starts from chance; but it masters and controls it, and gives it an active role. It thus manages to explain almost all the physico-chemical laws of our material world, and this hypothesis has become a marvelous if not universal tool.

* * *

To understand the old and much criticized theory of finalism we must look at nature from the point of view of evolution. We must not use a magnifying glass but must look at it from a distance, as if appreciating the beauty of a cathedral. In addition, the scale of time must be contracted and the mind must cover longer periods. It is above all important to try not to think too anthropomorphically.

If a microbe had a human intelligence, if he lived in the fold of an elephant's skin, and if his ancestors had created a science in a few generations—as ours have done—and had transmitted it to him, it is improbable that he would have a very clear idea of the laws that govern the movements of his universe: the elephant. He lives at the bottom of a valley five millimeters deep—equivalent to a canyon of ten or twelve thousand feet—and has created an image of the world very different from ours. When the elephant scratches himself, or takes a bath, the microscopic inhabitant of the valley is to be excused if he attributes these unpredictable cataclysms to very different causes. Let us try to avoid the point of view of the microbe, for whom one or two days—four generations—correspond to a century.

It is possible to conceive a finalistic hypothesis that is neither ridiculous nor in contradiction to our actual science. To do this, we need not even defend the hypothesis itself nor delve into its mechanism, which escapes us exactly as do the mechanisms of evolution, of the appearance of life, and of the birth of atoms.

First of all, we must not consider finalism as the inverse of determinism. In the latter, each event is the consequence of a previous series; it is determined by accomplished facts. This is clear. But in the hypothesis of finalism it is inexact to say that each event is determined by facts not yet accomplished. This would be nothing but a reversed determinism, with all the faults of determinism. In other words, this idea would be equivalent to the reversibility of determinism. Assuming that all the symbols were changed in our laws, which are symmetrical with respect to time, we would have no means of perceiving this fact (see p. 107) if the second principle of thermodynamics—the principle of entropy, quantitatively interpreted by the calculus of probabilities, foe of determinism—did not indicate the direction of the flow of time. Theoretically, therefore, the idea is not absurd. It is simply totally false.

By definition, finalism implies the existence of an end, of a goal to be reached, regardless of the means employed to attain it. It does not necessarily affirm that this end has been chosen by an all-powerful intelligence. This would be another hypothesis. It proposes a coordinating hypothesis, like evolution, like Einstein's curved and limited space, like the theory of an expanding universe, or like Schrödinger's probability waves.

The majority of men's actions are determined by an end. This is probably one of the reasons that has led to the conception of finalism. The idea of erecting indestructible pyramids in which to bury the Pharaohs was first conceived by one man. With this object in view, other men enslaved armies of human beings. Among the thousands who labored and suffered, how many at the beginning were conscious of the meaning of their efforts? Shall we say that their movements were determined? Shall we say that the construction of the pyramids, and their interior decorations, were determined in all their details? Or, shall we say that *the idea of erecting them* was determined? Either hypothesis is permissible. But if it was the idea alone that was first determined, then one can also say that this acted as an end from that moment on, which seems a simpler and more conceivable hypothesis.

The great navigators who started out to discover and colonize large and dangerous continents were led by an idea, as were the architects who built the cathedrals, the priests who battled for their faith, and the martyrs who submitted to torture. When a pilot who is at the helm of his boat at night, in a violent storm, battles contrary currents and succeeds in bringing his ship to port in spite of the elements, he has certainly been guided by a fixed idea that cannot be expressed in units of energy, but that nevertheless triumphs over the elements by the coordination it imposes.

Now, everything is determined for the determinist, including waves, currents, winds. This is mechanically conceivable. What is less conceivable is that another factor, which is infinitely weaker, from the energy point of view— assuming that it is appreciable at all—and which is equally determined by hypothesis, could resist all the enormous forces brought into play by the former and in the end triumph over them. No one ever imagined that it was the goal, namely, the return to port, that determined the succession of all the events from the beginning of the storm, considering that all these events tended to prevent this goal from being attained. Everyone, I think, is convinced that the will of the pilot dominates all the other factors. Now by what is this will determined, if it is determined? In other words, what in general determines the instinct of preservation in man? The pure determinist will at once object that there can be no instinct of preservation, as this notion presupposes a finality that he denies vigorously. And so logically—if this term can be applied to determinism—the will of the pilot is not determined in the sense of being a phenomenon that contributes to the prolongation of life.

Finalism, instead of limiting itself to immediate goals that are the great driving forces of man, modeling the terrestrial globe in order to adapt it to his needs, admits the existence of a single unknown, and probably unknowable, end—an end that has tended to realize itself since the beginning of the world. It is a kind of directing force which, instead of acting on the men of one era and during a short lapse of time, has acted and will continue to act on human beings in general for perhaps a billion years.

This force, this tendency—others call it will—does not manifest itself in details any more than the other forces of nature. It seems to have only *the result* in view. The average individual has no more reality for it than has the personality of an isolated molecule in the kinetic theory of gases, or in a crystal. An observer such as "Maxwell's demon," would certainly find some molecules in a gas-filled vessel that do not contribute individually to the maintenance of the pressure by striking against the sides. He might conclude that the kinetic theory is false. This is the attitude adopted by certain critics of finalism who, by a curious coincidence, are also the enemies of the modern statistical concepts. The hypothesis of finalism is, on the contrary, in rather good accord with the laws of chance: it only calls on the intervention of a minute energy capable of suppressing indetermination, or rather, capable of always influencing it in the same way. It is the anti-chance we spoke of on page 126.

That is the reason why "errors," or fluctuations, can occur, which on an average are compensated for in the end. The physical individual, as we said above, does not count. This may not be true for the intellectual, spiritual, or moral individual. It is, therefore, futile to collect cases of inadaptation or flagrant but accidental malformations, with the idea of disproving a hypothesis that is only valid on a statistical scale.

For example, the value of "instincts," as a means of perpetuating the species, has been discussed. It has been said that far from leading to the supreme goal, namely, the survival of the individual and the preservation of the species, they at times cause the death of the one and the degeneration of the other. This is sometimes true; but is it or is it not true that the species survive on an average?

It is the statistical mass result that counts, as in physics, and no one can deny it. Some people have tried to find an argument in the fact that when cows are loose in a field, they bloat themselves with clover or alfalfa until they die: there is, therefore, no instinct of conservation. These arguments are rather badly chosen, since domestic animals have been deprived by domestication of those instincts that they no longer need. I can well understand that people do not believe in finalism, but the arguments brought up against it do not, in general, harm it in the least.

The fact that strange, and apparently badly adapted, animals exist does not mean that the average is equally imperfect. It denotes that the ends and mechanisms of nature completely escape us. If transitory species disappear as did the dinosaurs, the apteryx, the dodo, and the mammoth, this does not mean that man, who occupies the top of the ladder and who is more recent, will disappear in his turn. But if he disappears he will perhaps be replaced by a being endowed with more intelligence or with a superior morality. We can very well conceive that man was an end, in comparison to the trilobite and to the *Tyranno-saurus rex* and that a form of superman is also an end in comparison to existing man who is still imperfect in so many ways.

It has been claimed that sexual instinct is not really destined to prolong the species, because it is not always directed to this end and because there are numerous aberrations. Nevertheless, it seems that everything has happened in the last few million years "as if" the species tended to persist, and that the impressive deviations we hear about have not prevented them from developing, on an average, "as if" they were really meant to develop. Let us avoid the limited anthropomorphic judgment, the point of view of the microbe on the elephant. If a species disappears, let us state that it has disappeared and let us try to understand how and why it did not persist. Let us follow the old precept of Epictetus and when we observe a fact let us not cast a judgment on another one that we do not know.

We cannot in good faith deny that the species that have disappeared have, on an average, been replaced by more complex, better-adapted, and more perfect ones. The fact that certain of them have not evolved, or have regressed, or disappeared, only proves that we know very little about the mechanism of evolution.

Everything points to the abrupt appearance of mammals. Certain reptiles have persisted. But there is a profound difference between reptiles and mammals, which is deeper even than the immense anatomical or physiological differences, a difference between the chemical structure of the serum proteins,[11] which makes the progressive passage from one class to another even more incomprehensible. Between birds and reptiles this difference is slight. We have here, as in the case of immunity, the indication of a deep chemical mechanism of evolution.

Let us not reproach nature for not being perfect according to the standards of perfection that she has given us. Let us not borrow arguments that apply to inferior classes (mollusks, amphibians, reptiles) and apply them to the mammal class. This procedure is definitely unscientific.

What do we gain by trying to prove that the eye is an imperfect instrument, of which Helmholtz was supposed to have said that if a constructor brought him such a defective instrument, he would refuse it. This is childish.

[11] P. and M. Lecomte du Noüy, *Contribution a l'étude des bases chimiques de la classification naturelle.* C.R. Soc. Biol., 1934, t. CXVI, p. 108.

Looking at it from a purely optical standpoint, we can say that no optician has ever been capable of constructing an objective of such wide angle. From a mechanical point of view, the focusing mechanism, which acts by a flattening or thickening of the lens, is simply prodigious. As far as the aperture of the objective is concerned, the diaphragm, represented by the truly circular iris, is very superior to the segmented diaphragm that we can manufacture. But the eye is more than that; it combines a retina, an optical nerve, brain cells that see, and, together with consciousness and intelligence, it has made possible the construction of optical instruments that may surpass it in certain respects but that cannot function without it.

Let us abandon these criticisms. To the unprejudiced observer the human body is an amazing masterpiece, not only from an anatomical point of view (muscles, articulations) and from a physiological point of view (metabolism in general, chemistry of the muscles, hormones, immunity, nervous system), but above all because it is the prop for human thought. In spite of its "very numerous blemishes and imperfections," and its sense organs "replete with imperfections" (Matisse), this thought enables it to criticize itself severely, as we have just seen. Now a determinist cannot think of separating consciousness from cerebral matter, which itself depends on all the physico-chemical phenomena constituting man. But as it is necessary before judging an imperfect thing to be more perfect, or to conceive greater perfection, which amounts to the same thing, this determinist will no doubt experience some difficulty in explaining the origin of the "purely fortuitous" determination of his criticism.

Professor Whitehead, speaking of the application of physical and chemical notions to the problems of life, expressed his point of view in a striking and ironical fashion: "The brilliant success of this method is admitted. But you cannot limit a problem by reason of a method of attack. The problem is to understand the operations of an animal body. There is clear evidence that certain operations of certain animal bodies depend upon the foresight of an end, and the purpose to attain it. It is no solution of the problem to ignore this evidence, because other operations have been explained in terms of physical and chemical laws. The existence of a problem is not even acknowledged. It is vehemently denied. Many a scientist has patiently designed experiments for the *purpose* of substantiating his belief that animal operations are motivated by no purposes. He has, perhaps, spent his spare time in writing articles to prove that human beings are as other animals, so that 'purpose' is a category irrelevant for the explanation of their bodily activities, his own activities included. *Scientists, animated by the purpose of proving that they are purposeless, constitute an interesting subject for study.*"

To sum up, we shall say that in the present state of science the hypothesis of finalism is not more absurd than any other, and that it has an immense advantage over the old determinism, by admitting as a working mechanism the same processes that are at the base of statistical laws. The calculus of probabilities can be applied. The notion of entropy is not contradictory, inasmuch as it ignores the end but imposes an evolution. The general scheme escapes our intelligence, we cannot grasp it at a glance. But a blind man does not deny the existence of the colors he cannot conceive; in the same way we cannot deny some sort of evolution in nature. The end is scientifically unknown to us, as are many other things. As early as the

Paleozoic period this end may have been the advent of abstract thought. In spite of the blunders with which the determinist severely reproaches nature, this goal has been attained. But seeing the use we make of it, we can imagine without presumption that the end is higher still.

It may be the advent of a perfect social state, but as insects, ants, bees, and termites have solved this problem, it is probable that the eventual goal is even more ambitious. The final end is perhaps the advent of a spiritually and morally superior human being whom we can hardly conceive at present. If so, we are very far from the goal, but we have hope.

We repeat that this conception of finalism does not contradict any of the data of modern science. However, it commits the crime of introducing an unknown parameter, an entelechy that cannot be expressed mathematically or incorporated into formulae. Undoubtedly this factor is inconceivable by means of pure intelligence. But human intelligence and consciousness are themselves totally inconceivable, yet we are obliged to admit them.

To give this observation its full value, I shall entrench myself behind the authority of Emile Borel[12] from whom I will again quote the following remarkable lines: "This contradiction (between the hidden but absolute determinism of molecular phenomena and determinism, on our scale of observation) being acknowledged, it will perhaps seem less strange to imagine that absolute beginnings can exist here and there, without being incompatible with scientific determinism. I must admit that this conception of absolute beginnings is extremely distasteful to me, as I suppose it is to all those who have had some scientific or even rational education. But my aversion to the theory of

[12] *Loc. cit.*, p. 296.

epiphenomenal consciousness is just as great, and this antinomy is the only philosophical problem that has never ceased to preoccupy me."

Finalism, on the other hand, is no more exempt from criticism than any other human hypothesis. However, the only criticisms that have come to my attention are not serious and are more sentimental than scientific. The objections that can be made to materialistic determinism are much more important, since they are based on discrepancies with facts and with the most probable and best-established theories of modern times. This explains the discredit into which it has fallen, and from which it has few chances of being raised. At present there is no hypothesis capable of explaining the birth of life and the development of consciousness without the intervention of a factor that can be described as extra-scientific or supernatural.

We have passed the age when we esteemed ourselves scientifically satisfied by elementary and childish comparisons between inorganic matter and life. "It seems to me that the thing which above all differentiates biology and physics," said Gabriel Lippmann, the great physicist, in talking to Guye, "is that in living things we have apparatus (pumps, systems of circulation, optical instruments, etc.)—in short, organs; whereas in all inorganic nature we see only phenomena."

But to me it seems that the thing that, above all, differentiates biology and physics is that life has culminated in thought, which in turn has *created* biology and physics.

It is surprising how easily eminent men underestimate their intelligence when they try to explain its mechanism, and overestimate it when, having failed to do so, they refuse to admit the possibility of an outside cause, or a cause foreign to the rational realm that they have erected. Even those who believe neither in evolution nor in its continuity say: "Wait, in two or three or ten centuries we shall have explained everything; we have hardly started." They thus show a wonderful confidence in this continuity that they combat only because it does not enter into the actual framework of our intellectual concepts.

During the last few years we have witnessed a real revolution in science and in human concepts. For centuries, even millenniums, the vast swing of the pendulum was directed toward the region dominated by the anguish of primitive man. The ignorance of elementary facts forbade any intelligent interpretation of the perils with which humanity felt itself to be surrounded. For the immense majority of men life was a daily struggle. They did not know at dawn whether the night would find them victorious or vanquished. This precarious existence, unceasingly menaced, was bound to lead to superstitions that were exploited by a small group who were better endowed intellectually and, therefore, less terrorized than the crowd. When human knowledge progressed, the pendulum swung back in the other direction toward science, taking its impetus from the very excesses to which its preceding course had carried it. This time it reached the end of its swing toward the beginning of our century—in less than three hundred years. We are now witnessing the beginning of the new oscillation, which has acquired considerable speed in the last few years. The reversal of direction, the replacing of the old Newtonian ideas by others, was brutal. Not quite sixty years have elapsed since Tyndall asserted in his Belfast speech that science alone could solve all human problems. Twenty years have hardly passed since the great materialist, Bertrand Russell, speaking of the answers of science, said that "Only on the firm foundation of unyielding despair can the soul's habitation henceforth be safely built." [13]

Human science is a series of structures bound together by logic. These structures are expressed by numbers and ratios born in our consciousness. But our states of consciousness furnish us with qualitative data that science ignores. Everything that is qualitative can, it is true, be translated by our brain in two ways: by a number and by an impression. A sunset "seen" by a photo-electric exposure meter is expressed by a number read on the dial, and by an impression of beauty, which is just as real, even though we cannot express it scientifically. The essence of our intellectual and sentimental life escapes the quantitative symbolism we have created, and all efforts to try to link vital manifestations to the structural and functional complexities of living organisms have failed. They could not succeed, as these are two realms that, in the actual state of science, are separated. It is generally admitted that the complexity of behavior of a living being is linked to the complexity of the nervous system. This observation led to the creation of a theory that had a period of popularity:

[13] This passage can be compared to another text by the same author: "That man is the product of causes which had no prevision of the end they were achieving; that his origin, his growth, his hopes and fears, his loves and beliefs, are but the outcome of accidental collocations of atoms; that no fire, no heroism, no intensity of thought and feeling, can preserve an individual life beyond the grave; that all the labors of the ages, all the devotion, all the inspiration, all the noon-day brightness of human genius, are destined to extinction in the vast death of the solar system, and that the whole temple of Man's achievement must inevitably be buried beneath the debris of a universe in ruins—all these things, if not quite beyond dispute, are yet so nearly certain, that no philosophy which rejects them can hope to stand." I do not think that any philosopher or any poet has ever expressed with greater anguish, eloquence, and force the cruel creed of the materialist.

behaviorism. This theory simply suppresses thought but encounters serious difficulties in trying to explain Pavlov's conditioned reflexes. Some authors who criticized it—Dr. Broad among others—did not hesitate to qualify it as absurd. This much is certain: the relation between the complexity of an individual's behavior and that of the nervous system is far from being clearly established. The bee, the ant, the spider, for example, give proof of extremely complicated instincts, even though the organization of their nervous system is relatively simple, whereas the instincts of other animals that are endowed with a much more complicated nervous system, such as certain mammals, are much less remarkable.

The prophecies of the materialists ranging from Laplace and Tyndall to Bertrand Russell's pathetic profession of faith no longer seem so convincing now that the progress in nuclear physics—the physics of electrons and protons— enables us to perceive new problems and the vast extent of our ignorance.

The profession of a prophet is very hazardous because the method employed is *always* extrapolation. I have already shown its dangers, which are especially great when the conclusions lead the author, without his knowledge, from one realm to another. I know that this is precisely what the prophet refuses to admit: he does not conceive that two separate realms can exist. But the scientist asks experimental proof of what is advanced; and the prophet is incapable of supplying it. He bases his stand therefore on a postulate that is in fact an undemonstrable act of faith. This is perfectly admissible, when it is a question of edifying a purely logical system—geometry, for example. But to "explain" the properties of the electrons it was necessary, in spite of the rigor of Euclid's geometry, to have recourse to a totally different geometry that was no longer three-dimensional but pluri-dimensional. One might think that a single electron represents a material unit, as its "accompanying wave train" occupies a three-dimensional space. But the associated waves of two electrons require a six-dimensional space, those of three electrons require a nine-dimensional space and so forth. Einstein's theory also imposes a space that is no longer Euclidean but is governed by Riemann's geometry, which takes no account of Euclid's postulate. Shall we, therefore, say that this postulate is false? No; for one reason, because it enabled us to develop a geometry that applies perfectly to all our preceptible universe, and for another, because our mind refuses to conceive more than three spatial dimensions. This is a criterion of "reality." But it is no longer valid in another conceptual realm that the prophet is forced to admit for the time being. We have not yet succeeded in passing from one to the other. But neither have we succeeded, until now, in passing from the unorganized realm to the organized world, that is, to life, nor from life to thought. Any assertion that does not take these facts into account has no scientific value, and has neither more nor less importance than astrological predictions published in the newspapers.

FACING OUR RESPONSIBILITIES

Argument

Like a stream following its course, humanity slowly progresses toward unknown ends. A people or a nation are represented through the centuries by their outstanding individuals. The principal role of the mass is to give birth to these individuals and foster their development.

In the beginning men lived in terror of their enemies, of the unknown forces of nature, and turned for protection to the war lords and to the priests. A conflict was certain to arise between these two powers. The spiritual leaders, with their greater hold on the people, conquered the war lords but in turn became the chief enemy of the revolutionary leaders. The latter first attacked the priests and the Church, and finally, the very idea of God. They based their arguments on science. Yet modern science can only supply relative answers and is forced to call upon "anti-chance," which one might well call God. And so we are faced again with Pascal's famous wager.

The true crisis is a moral crisis. We must hope that man will understand that the civilization in which he takes such pride will collapse unless it rests on more solid foundations.

7

FACING OUR RESPONSIBILITIES

> Men are not taught to be honest, but they are
> taught everything else; yet they pride themselves
> on honesty above all things. Thus they flatter
> themselves on knowing the one thing they have
> not learned.
>
> —Pascal

Human beings live in a realm untouched by science. It is
the domain of appetites, passions, sentiments, aestheticism,
and morals. The only truth in this realm is what we perceive and what we feel.

A child is in direct contact with nature. He has been
hereditarily adapted to it for hundreds of centuries. He
reacts emotionally to the new facts introduced by progress.
Nobody questions the reality of his joys, sorrows, and ambitions. These are the elements that build up his personality
by degrees. It is his personality that differentiates him from
a colloidal particle jostled about by the Brownian movement; it is again his personality that can eventually influence the fate of a people or steer a part of humanity into
a different course.

There is the same difference between the picture of a man projected by science and the reality of this man, as there is between the detailed plan of a small town and the private life of its citizens. The pink polygons that represent dwellings, factories, or farmhouses on scale do not bring us into contact with the dramas of love, jealousy, and greed that constitute the other aspect of the town. They give us no inkling of the psychological side.

There are two points of view: that of the geographer or surveyor, and that of Balzac. They are often correlative. But if Balzac met the surveyor, they could both talk for hours about the same village, without being aware of it. But for man and for the society of which he is a part, it is Balzac's view that dominates. It is the only one that counts.

What does a stranger mean when he speaks of "France"? He can have in his mind's eye a succession of motion pictures that remind him of an automobile trip through the country—pictures accompanied by the train of his aesthetic reactions. But he can also evoke France as a nation, from the standpoint of its prestige and role in the evolution of European civilization during the past thousand years. The name of "France," which then comprises forty or fifty succeeding generations, corresponds in this case merely to a hundred individuals at most; some great kings, Napoleon, several great painters, sculptors, musicians, a few great writers and philosophers, certain great scientists and soldiers, and a small number of statesmen. That is "France." The six or seven hundred million Frenchmen who were born and died during this period come into the picture only as a background or as the anonymous mass that follows its leaders or revolts to follow other leaders. If we eliminate, in thought, these hundred-odd individuals, we eradicate from the history of civilization one of its most brilliant elements, one in which we take the greatest pride. We drag France down to the level of the tribes of Central China, India, and Africa.

The part played by the mass of the people is not limited to eating, working for a living, or blindly following its leader. Its most important role consists in producing great men; the great men who will guide the people's hesitating steps and will represent the qualities that, later on, will be attributed to the entire population.

But we can no more find the qualities and virtues of great men in the crowd from which they emerged than we can find the biological properties of a protein in the thousands of atoms that constitute it. The most we can say is that some ethnical groups contain scattered characteristics that certain individuals possess to a high degree.

The motives that stir the crowd are sometimes physiological: hunger. More often they are ideological: faith, hate, patriotism, the desire to take or to destroy. Hunger, the only true physiological motive that may be considered excusable, is not as powerful as the others. In occidental countries, a large number of men do not often suffer from hunger at the same time. However, recent events in Europe have shown that such a contingency can arise.[1] In some oriental countries famine exists in an endemic state. This, combined with other factors, has brought about the development of inferior races that no longer produce leaders. Superstition and the domination of superior races maintain this state of affairs.

The world is governed by passions and ideas. But passions are not efficacious unless they are directed. This is possible only through the impelling thought and will of a

[1] These lines were written in 1938. The author little thought that in a short time this catastrophe would cover the whole of Europe. P. L. N.

leader who, from this point of view, plays the role of a catalyzer. If we spill a large number of matches in disorder on the table and light the heap at the four corners, they will burn rather slowly, hardly less so than ordinary bits of wood. But if someone takes the trouble to arrange the matches one by one, with all the phosphorated ends on the same side and then applies a lighted match, there will be a flare. Certain individuals are endowed with this power of orienting, at pleasure, what men call their "will."

Like a stream following its course, humanity slowly progresses toward unknown ends. But a stream sometimes encounters irregular ground on its way and is forced to tumble from a great height. We know that man can no more oppose the current that sweeps him along than a drop of water can return to its source. The immense majority of molecules, which make up the mass of water, are not separated from it by the fall. But the effervescence of the cascade throws up a certain number that form an ethereal veil, a liquid dust, a mist exempt from the laws governing the shape and the direction of the river. A sunbeam pierces the clouds, and behold! a rainbow emerges out of the mist. The iridescent cloud springs from the cascade but the cascade itself is lustreless and gray; only the droplets are ablaze in a glory of color.

Likewise the artistic and intellectual capital of a country, of a race, is due to a relatively small number of individuals who have risen above the crowd. Their consciousness, instead of simply perceiving nature without reacting, or, if one prefers, instead of reflecting the light like a mirror, breaks up and refracts it into its colored elements. The waterfall, the whole river, glory in the rainbow. Yet the question has sometimes arisen whether it is not the ponderous, shapeless mass of the stream that should be given primary consideration, for at the bottom it is this mass that traces its path to the sea and operates the mills. One forgets that turbines had to be invented before its force could be utilized.

This is one of the fundamental differences between societies of insects and human society. The former have reached such a remarkable degree of perfection that we cannot conceive how they could progress farther. They are fixed—as far as we can judge—as though, their purpose being attained, there was nothing left for them to do but to multiply indefinitely in a rigid, unalterable frame. Individuality no longer exists. It is impossible to know whether it ever existed. There is no place for it. Specialization is pushed to the extreme: there are workmen, soldiers, the queen, males. . . . The only individual entity worthy of the name is the community, the hive, the anthill, the termitarium. This individual, on our scale of observation, behaves like a soulless body. We would have to study it for several thousand years to understand it.

In our very imperfect human society it is the individual, on the contrary, who dominates; and as rivalries arise between individuals, they throw the masses that follow them against each other. The lives of millions of men and the very equilibrium of the world can be menaced by the ambition and will of a single malevolent brain.

The crisis that is shaking the world is profound. Its origin is not difficult to discover; it lies in the fact that the development of knowledge has been far greater than the development of man's moral qualities. By development I mean not only progress but its propagation, which entails dangerous deformations.

No matter how far back we go in history, we always find the existence of religions, sometimes crude, but always attempting to establish rules of communal life. They all base their authority and prestige on mysteries, which only the initiated are supposed to pierce. This is the most natural and direct method of impressing the crowd, whose ignorance has always been exploited for this purpose.

The forces of nature—lightning and thunder, cyclones, earthquakes—feared by all living beings, were understandably used in the beginning by those who had enough intelligence to perceive the advantages that could be derived from them, even though they dreaded them and were ignorant of their origin, just as the mass of the people did. Moral ideas, as we comprehend them, were probably not very clear at the beginning of human society. The instincts of man, very similar to those of the animals, smothered the vacillating lights, which in the course of centuries were to transform themselves into moral ideas.

The struggle for life was more than an empty phrase during these periods when all nature appeared to be leagued against this frail being, who lacked means of defense or attack. It was natural that terror should be the dominant sentiment and that men should instinctively gather around the individuals who seemed less open to fear. They were the "priests," if they can be so called, the men who, in the imagination of the people, were capable of acting as intermediaries between themselves and the menacing powers of nature.

A conflict was bound to arise between the two authorities followed by the people, the war lord who by his strength and physical bravery imposed himself as the best fitted to defend them against other men and wild beasts; and the leader who was more intelligent but less strong physically and less courageous, who pretended to be able to defend them against cataclysms, against the obscure, mysterious, and direful forces of nature. The fact that the war lord himself was as impressed—and often as terrorized—as his people and inclined occasionally to solicit the help and protection of the "priest," only made this conflict more acute. A covert but often cruel war was thus born between their two powers: the power due to physical prestige, inherited from the ancestor, derived from the example of animals; and the more subtle intellectual power, based on the mysterious prestige of knowledge and on the exploitation of ignorance, which truly characterizes *homo sapiens*.

Gradually, as the centuries passed, these two authorities evolved and perfected themselves, never ceasing to combat each other, with alternating success on both sides. Their prestige had become considerable and they could not resist the temptation of trying to use their authority for a personal or corporative interest, according to the individual qualities of their representatives.

On the other hand, from time to time, men were born amongst the people who would formerly have become leaders or priests through their intrinsic qualities. Endowed with more than average intelligence, they revolted against the excesses of the two directing classes. They represented a new foe against whom it was necessary to organize, for they menaced the painfully acquired privileges that could have been renounced by men of superhuman virtue alone.

The qualities of the rebel were sometimes real. As a result of the degeneration of the leaders and of the increase in favoritism, which had insensibly substituted inferior men for true leaders, the too-long-established hierarchy had lost its power. The people who learned through the lips of the newcomer the extent of their misfortune and

suffering—of which they were not always aware—followed
him blindly as soon as he had succeeded in imposing his
will by deceiving them into the belief that he intended to
lead them to the desired goal. The established order was
overthrown. In the joy and enthusiasm that always accompany destruction, arson, plunder, rape, and murder, the
new leader attempted to reconstruct a kingdom. He sometimes succeeded at the price of blood. Often it was another
who benefited from his efforts, at a time when the crowd
itself was saturated with carnage. And so the same tale
repeated itself with different actors.

The war lord, the king, his aids and family were usually
swept away in the adventure because their authority
rested merely on material strength, which was now distributed amongst a bodyguard, an army, and officers in
their pay. The revolutionary leader was able to oppose
this force with a force of like nature. The strongest, or the
best organized of the two, was bound to win. The strength
of the king, the physical symbol of the government, was
represented in a tangible form by number and arms which
no longer impressed the rebels, but the force of the priests,
who retained secret and mysterious powers, had steadily
been reinforced in an occult and underground manner.
They were shrewder and recognized that their strength
depended less on quantity than on quality, less on their
bravery than on the ancestral fear of men, less on real
science than on its prestige, less on their own knowledge
than on the ignorance of others.

Thus a tremendous power had developed that was not
dependent upon any particular individuals and against
which the rebels were helpless. For if the high priest and
his associates were killed, other leaders immediately sprang
up who, though apparently new, were in reality children

of the same tradition—the intellectual tradition. This power, conscious not only of its intellectual superiority but of the superiority it derived from being self-perpetuating, was obviously bound to conceive the ambitious plan of dominating the king, of selecting him, and, in short, of reigning in actual fact.

This resulted in new conflicts from which sometimes one side, sometimes the other, emerged as conquerors. But the victories of the kings and of the war lords crushed only temporarily the anonymous authority that smoldered beneath the ashes, whereas the triumphs of the priests slowly sapped the royal prestige, which could no longer be defended except by tradition and individual valor.

In their struggle, the priests leaned on the people whom they easily maneuvered. The isolated rebel chiefs understood the danger, and a hatred was born that is far from being quenched today. For they felt that they were once more fighting with inferior weapons, and that suffering, even hunger, are less powerful levers than the ideas, the forms of mysticism, that were progressively emerging. It was the dawn of secret lay societies, inspired, even in their rites, by religious organizations.

Men had existed in all ages who seemed to be created of nobler matter and who embodied all the virtues of humanity. They not only possessed these virtues and put them into practice but they derived the new notion of duty from them. Thus morality appeared timidly here and there, shedding its ephemeral glow like the first fireflies on a dark spring night.

Whence does this strange notion arise? What is its source? As Ernest Renan said: "Morality in humanity is analogous to the maternal instincts of birds. It is the blind sacrifice of self to an unknown end, willed by nature.

Duty and the instinct of the brood have the same providential origin. The universe, to which we are related as by an umbilical cord, demands devotion, duty, virtue; to obtain its end it employs religion, poetry, love, pleasure, all the illusions. Everything is comprised in a faith in those instincts that obsess us without convincing us. Its orders are clear; its promises obscure."

The strength of these superior beings, who were not superhuman but on the contrary more profoundly human than the others, lay in their sincerity and their disinterestedness. Most men are not very familiar with these virtues but they are sometimes capable of divining them, not so much by the intermediary of words but directly, by a kind of resonance whose mechanism escapes us. For a long time such men were so few and so feeble, so isolated, that nobody took offense. Then their number increased: they were the prophets who soon became the martyrs.

Mysticism developed in the most diverse places: in China, in India, in Egypt, and assumed varying forms, depending on climate, customs, and the times. But all these forms apparently imbibed their inspiration at the same source. Their teachings were almost identical and this identity constitutes an astounding problem.

The spiritual element thus made its appearance in the world. It is hardly probable that its development preceded the upsurge of mysticism. It is, of course, possible but our scanty knowledge of prehistoric times does not justify such an affirmation.

The immense superiority of mysticism, which made it at the same time a dangerous weapon for the established order and a marvelous tool to influence the masses, arose from the fact that it showed men the road to happiness. It taught them that the source of felicity is internal and not external; that happiness lies in justice and virtue; that unhappiness lies in evil; that physical suffering is the best means of attaining the moral perfection in which happiness and peace of the soul reside; that man is free to elevate or to lower himself, and that nobody on earth can deprive him of this, the only true liberty.

Addressing itself as it did to pariahs, to slaves surfeited with suffering, lowered to the level of beasts, this language was certain to awaken an echo that resounded in our occidental world until the Middle Ages—and even later. Christian mysticism reigned freely. The Apostolic Roman Catholic Church, which had been built on it, triumphed. Kings bowed down before it.

But the Church was composed of men who did not all have prophets' souls nor martyrs' hearts. Human nature varies little in the course of centuries. The amazing prestige of the Church, her undisputed strength and ever-increasing opulence, were destined to attract the direct descendants of the priests of former times, those who saw in sacred institutions primarily a means of domination and good living. They were numerous and sometimes intelligent. By degrees, they took over the levers of command, which the others, the sincere ones, were only too happy to abandon in order to devote themselves to contemplation, prayer, or charity.

The Church progressively became a vast administrative machine, jealous of its prerogatives and of its authority, convinced of its infallibility' even in questions unrelated to dogma. When it encountered individuals who dared to think independently in certain fields, it often looked on them with a suspicious eye. When, furthermore, these individuals were geometers and asserted, in contradiction to current beliefs, that the world turned around the sun, they became not only suspect but dangerous and were even burned.

This was an error. At a period when a reawakening of human curiosity, soon to flower into the scientific spirit, could be observed on all sides, this intransigent attitude was shortsighted. It alienated a goodly number of the very people the Church should have called to her bosom. The clergy should have understood that all attacks on freedom of thought, when neither morals nor dogma were concerned, made enemies of the very people it most needed. The Church became frightened; it doubted.

War was not openly declared during the 17th century, a period characterized by an extraordinary group of philosophers and scientists. The Church was still strong. As soon as Descartes heard of Galileo's condemnation in Rome, he took to his heels and rushed to his publishers to stop his *Principles of Philosophy* from appearing in print. In this treatise, which was not published until fourteen years after his death by his friend Clerselier, Descartes defended ideas similar to those of Galileo.

The Church should have understood, as I said in the Foreword, that she had nothing to fear from discoveries; that, to a believer, a well-established fact is necessarily of divine essence and that only human theories superimposed on physical phenomena can, when they are false, be dangerous. She should have understood that only the rigorous control of scientific facts is of moment, and therefore should have tried to assist this control. She should have understood that human curiosity and ingenuity cannot be shackled, and that it would be wiser to take them into partnership than frequently to fight them. She apparently underestimated intelligence and overestimated her own strength; and yet it is intelligence that is divine.

The Church soon perceived that some of the new forces were not to be scorned—and so the struggle began. In France, the appearance of the Encyclopedists toward the middle of the 18th century was the signal for the outbreak of a war that gravely undermined the prestige of the Church in that country. The strength of the Egyptian, Babylonian, and even Greek priests came from the fact that they encouraged and utilized the mathematicians and the "philosophers of nature." The priests had thus established a more or less complete "trust" of the intellectual and of the miraculous, of reason and of irrationalism. They could at the same time guide the mind and the heart. The Church was suspicious of the new trend of reason because it developed outside her realm, and she did not see how rapidly the situation had changed since Gutenberg. When the printing press was invented, she had realized that this new means of diffusion must be closely watched. The necessity of the "Imprimatur" was a proof of this. But she had not foreseen that the great diffusion of books would make the material realization of this control impossible in practice.

Books progressively undermined clerical authority; at first less by direct attacks than by the diffusion of knowledge and the exercise of the intellectual faculties, which reading encouraged. A greater number of men learned to think. They familiarized themselves with this prodigious tool, the brain, and they became drunk with their discovery. The ground was prepared for the teachings of the Encyclopedists, of Voltaire, and of Rousseau; the smallest seeds sprouted and reproduced rapidly.

They proliferated quickly because the sense of criticism had not developed in a parallel manner, because novelty always possesses a considerable attraction and because men had already suffered a long time from the constraint put upon them. They thought they had been bullied and deceived, and that an attempt had been made to imprison them in artificial molds. Was there "something else" that had been concealed from them? The magic word "liberty," which was coming into fashion, lost the purely spiritual meaning given it by the mystics and prophets, because men had learned, through books, that they possessed an unsuspected power, the power of what they considered "rational" reasoning.

A frenzy of learning and of discussion slowly invaded the upper classes. The consequent excitement lasted until about the end of the 19th century and resulted in the most naïve philosophical extrapolations. Moral ideas were progressively blurred, tending to disappear completely in the dazzling light of a new star.

This shining liberating star was science. The Church had looked upon it with suspicion from the very first, and as this suspicion had occasionally materialized in a rather brutal manner, its adorers, almost without exception, considered the clergy as their foe. At first they only fought the priests and not religion nor the idea of God. The number of those who used science as an argument against religion itself increased during the 19th century. It increased more rapidly as soon as it became apparent that a mysticism cannot be suppressed unless it is replaced by another. It was a splendid occasion for those who were not real scientists, but who were ambitious, to use science as a springboard to destroy totally the secular prestige of the Church, against which they had vainly struggled for so long.

The age-old conflict was not dead. The king, the priests, and those who were neither one nor the other, but considered themselves superior to both, still existed and will always exist. In France, for instance, the opposition first of all suppressed the king. This was the easiest task, for, as in the time of the Egyptians, the priests represented a many-headed hydra. Then they bethought themselves of organizing the struggle against the Church, which had aroused in the whole country what might be termed an "allergy to priests."

At this stage science came to the rescue. The support it innocently gave to all those who were discontented and bitter was considerable. The honest scientist of the period worked day and night in his laboratory without any other desire than to understand nature. But there was the scientific philosopher who did little research work, and the fantasy and exaggeration of his conclusions made them all the more impressive. There was the abstract philosopher, always impressed by the importance of science: understanding nothing of its nature, he felt qualified to dwell on it at length. There was also the descendant of the old rebel—arrogant, badly educated, yet intelligent and ambitious—whose only thought was to use science and scientists in order to fight his all-time enemy, the priest, and eventually to take his place. Finally, there was a small number of sincere reformers who in the abstract desired the happiness of their fellow men and who were swept along like wisps of straw in the current.

Renan, in spite of his great honesty and profound intelligence, was duped by the mirage. Later, however, he lost confidence. His arguments are those of the man in the street. "Science," he writes, "enables us to seek the Truth; more than that, it brings us the only possibility of improving our material fate. . . . Finally, it preserves us from error. It is already something not to be duped. The man who is trained by its disciplines is definitely more admirable than the sentient man belonging to the age of faith. He is exempt from errors into which the uneducated person is inevitably led. He is more enlightened, he commits fewer crimes, he is less sublime and less absurd. One can say that this is no compensation for the Paradise that science takes away. Who knows if science takes it away? After all, no one is impoverished when worthless bonds and counterfeit money are taken out of his pocketbook. A little good science is better than much bad science. We err less when confessing our ignorance than when we imagine we know many things we do not know."

These lines are taken from the preface to *The Future of Science*. It is easy to detect the uneasiness of an honest man, who at a ripe age feels the urge to convince himself and to absolve himself for having made a choice based on motives that, deprived of the support given them by the passion of youth, appear rather frail to serve as a prop for the lever of reason.

But Renan falls into the error common to all philosophers, theoreticians, and writers of that period. He thinks he speaks of Man when in reality he is speaking of Renan, and he forgets that humanity produces very few Renans. He again errs when he seems to consider that educated man is better than "the sentient man of the age of faith"; he endows science with attributes of morality that it does not possess. We shall shortly see that he acknowledges this fact.

"He commits fewer crimes." How evident it is that this passage was written in the 19th century! "A little good science is better than much bad science." I have shown in the first part of this book what is left of the "little good science" of 1848.

Finally: "We err less in confessing our ignorance."
But has a little science, even if good, ever led anyone to
acknowledge his ignorance? On the contrary, the less man
knows of science the more he clings to what he thinks are
his ideas. A wide knowledge is needed to judge impartially
and few men are capable of assimilating this wide knowledge. The proof of this is given by the superficial minds
that flourish today. Renan thought that science would
diffuse light because it had explained eclipses, thunder,
and a few other phenomena that had terrorized humanity
of old. He did not suspect that "much science" would re-
open many questions and would propound still graver
problems, inasmuch as we cannot at present conceive that
they can ever be solved by the human brain.

I quote this remarkably intelligent man because he
symbolizes the tendencies of his epoch, mistaking knowledge for judgment; the two have no common measure.
We read further: "Our true reason for defending primary
education is that a people without instruction is fanatic,
and that a fanatical race always creates a danger for
science, as governments are in the habit of imposing in-
tolerable constraints on freedom of mind."

There is a strange innocence in these lines. To begin
with, he confuses the people with the government, whereas
the two have never had anything in common. Secondly,
he seems to think that nations can become fanatic by
themselves, which is false; a nation is fanaticized by a
fanatic. There is no evidence that a mass of men has ever
spontaneously developed any kind of fanaticism without
a leader. Finally, did he really imagine that primary education suffices to kill fanaticism? It is difficult to admit.

Individual fanatics will always exist, just as lunatics,
criminals, and thieves will always exist, and it is the fanatic

who is dangerous—not the idea he takes as his text. Renan was rightly indignant over the sad consequences of religious fanaticism; it is a pity that he did not live long enough to contemplate the dreadful excesses of anti-religious fanaticism.

Neither instruction nor reason suffices to smother in man certain revolting ancestral tendencies, nor to kill the cruelty that is hidden in the individual but that bursts forth as soon as the crowd guarantees anonymity. No matter what origin we attribute to moral ideas, they are at the base of civilized societies, and they always have to struggle against strange enemies, rooted in the innermost depths of man ever since his appearance on earth. Even today we must still beware of those sinister impulses that prompted man to create stone images with an impassive smile and knees slimy with blood.

It is, alas, impossible to suppress fanaticism or to give to all men the wide culture necessary to judge impartially. Though we might admit that the elementary culture given by primary education could become impartial, it can never succeed in forming men's judgment. This is equally true of the semi-culture given by higher education. The error consists in thinking that the rare faculty of judging sanely and freely must be the natural consequence of a few years of standardized cramming, for which a great majority of children are neither physiologically nor morally fit.

Since we have spent some time discussing the preface to *The Future of Science* and since it has given us glimpses of the public opinion of those days, let us continue its perusal so that we may understand both Renan's good faith and his struggles of conscience. These remarkable and little-known lines prove that the problem of morality already existed at a time when materialistic and positivistic fervor were at their height, and that Renan himself had lost confidence in science as a universal solution. They are impressively alive.

On examining his manuscript before sending it to the publisher, he took stock of himself: "A warm current relaxed my severity; almost all my illusions of 1848 crumbled and appeared impossible. I saw the fatal necessities of human society; I resigned myself to a state of creation in which a great deal of evil conditions a little good, in which an imperceptible quantity of aroma is extracted from an enormous *caput mortuum* of wasted material. I reconciled myself in several respects with reality and when, on my return, I reviewed the book I had written a year before, I found it bitter, dogmatic, sectarian and harsh . . .

". . . The idea of a civilization based on equality, as evoked by certain pages of this work, is, then, a dream. A school in which the pupils would make the laws would be a sorry school. Light, morality, and art will always be represented in humanity by a magistracy, by a minority, guarding the tradition of truth, goodness, and beauty. But in order to maintain its power, this magistracy should not have recourse to impostures and superstitions nor be allowed to dispose of force.

"There were also many illusions in the accord I gave, in those ancient days, to the socialistic ideas of 1848. Though I still believe that science alone can ameliorate the sad condition of man, here below, I no longer believe the solution of the problem to be as near as I thought it then. Inequality is written in Nature; it is the consequence of liberty, and individual liberty is a necessary postulate of human progress. This progress implies great sacrifice of individual happiness. The actual state of humanity, for

216 . THE ROAD TO REASON

example, requires the maintenance of nations, which are very heavy establishments to carry. A state that would give individuals the greatest possible happiness would probably be a state of profound degradation from the point of view of the noble pursuits of humanity.

". . . Between the two objectives of political concepts, greatness of nations or well-being of individuals, we choose through interest or through passion. We have no indication of the will of Nature nor of the goal of the universe. For us, the idealists, only one single doctrine is true; the transcendant doctrine according to which the purpose of humanity is the development of a superior conscience, or, as was said formerly, 'the greatest glory of God.' But this doctrine could not serve as a practical political goal. Such an objective must, on the contrary, be carefully dissimulated. Men would revolt if they knew they were thus exploited.

". . . To sum up: though the incessant work of the 19th century has greatly increased the knowledge of facts, the destiny of mankind has become more obscure than ever. The grave problem of the future is that we do not see how humanity can be given in the future a sufficiently satisfactory catechism, without a return to credulity. It is therefore possible that the downfall of idealistic beliefs is destined to follow the downfall of supernatural beliefs, and that a real abasement of morals dates from the day on which humanity saw the reality of things. It had been possible to obtain, by means of myths, a surprisingly high moral effort from the kindhearted gorilla; take away the myths, and a part of the simulated energy that they awakened will disappear.

". . . I say frankly: I cannot imagine how the foundations of a noble and happy life will be rebuilt without the

ancient dreams. The hypothesis in which the true sage
is the one who neglects wider horizons and confines his
outlook to vulgar pleasures is absolutely repugnant to us.
But it is not the first time that the happiness and nobility
of man appear unstable. Let us continue to enjoy the
supreme gift that has been bestowed on us: that of existing
and of contemplating reality." [2]

It is superfluous to comment on these lines, which are
well worth meditating.

Let us see if there was justification for Renan's dis-
illusionment at the beginning of our century. The fight
between spiritual authority and its enemies, dating from
many centuries earlier, continued. But spiritual power,
the bulwark of morality, had lost its intellectual prestige
by not accepting the power of science—reinforced by the
output of the printing press. The unruly child had become
a man who vindictively remembered his shackles and
chastisements. By the end of the 19th century, the primitive
bow and arrow had been transformed into machine guns.
The conflict still smoulders beneath the ashes, illuminated
here and there by revealing sparks. The only exceptions
in Europe are the countries in which the third power, that
of the king, or the government, has kept its authority based
on love, moral force, and confidence. The scientist is often
a "freethinker"; in other words, he has liberated himself from the discipline of the Church. He feels he has
progressed. He denies the necessity of the hypothesis
"God." The simplicity of a theory appears to him a proof
of its veracity. All extrapolations seem legitimate. The

[2] This last paragraph can be compared to the following passage by Henri
Poincaré: "For myself . . . I want neither this avid and narrow plutocracy
nor this virtuous and mediocre democracy, solely occupied in turning the
left cheek and peopled by sages who, devoid of curiosity and avoiding excesses, would die, not of illness, but, unquestionably, of boredom."

supernatural is no longer in vogue, or rather, miracles have been replaced by other phenomena that he claims to explain scientifically. Human reason, and above all rationalism, have inherited the prestige that was formerly the appendage of the priest and, in the light of this apotheosis, the apparent death of moral tradition passes almost unnoticed. What little remained alive in private families was sufficient to give the false illusion that it could be dispensed with. It took one or two generations for this progressive deficiency to be felt.

Science takes giant strides. The new concept of comfort appears first in the form of an agreeable luxury. By degrees it becomes a necessity that makes slaves of us. The remarkable evolution of medicine under the influence of a man of genius, Pasteur, fires the imagination and spares needless suffering; mortality decreases. Pain is vanquished by anaesthetics. Sterile surgery strips the operating room of its terrors. Man accomplishes near miracles. The means of communication are multiplied; velocity increases, distances decrease; aviation conquers the sky, brings towns nearer together, compresses the oceans. Wireless telegraphy increases the safety of travel, the radio eliminates time by establishing an instantaneous contact between all points of the globe. Finally, moving pictures raise the veils that existed between classes and reveal to all men the beauty, as well as the sordidness, of humanity. At the same time, weapons become deadlier, shells are heavier and more destructive, guns shoot accurately at a distance of seventy-five miles; yperite (mustard gas) makes its appearance. It is not yperite that is frightful, but the use people have dared to make of it, constituting one of the greatest crimes man has committed against himself.

With the exception of pure scientific work, namely, the activity of a small number of individuals, there is nothing in all this that, by itself, constitutes an element capable of raising or maintaining the moral level of a nation. We need only to look around us to be convinced of it. Life has certainly become easier, less dangerous.[3] Everything tends to lessen exertion, at the same time standardizing pleasures, ambitions, and inclinations. Instead of trying to satisfy his true aspirations—those that are the consequence of his physiological and moral ego—the man in the street, the average citizen, turns, in spite of himself, to occupations that he is not always free to choose, and to pleasures that, without his realizing it, are imposed on him by the mere fact that he lives in society. Magazines, movies, the radio, show him fantastic examples of careers which tempt him but to which he is not adapted. If, as usually happens, he does not succeed in modeling his life on these pictures, he deems himself badly used and unhappy, and his existence is nothing but a perpetual discontent. He overlooks the real joys within his grasp and cannot conceive life without the material advantages enjoyed by his neighbors, or even by the inhabitants of remote countries. Jealousy intervenes. He no longer desires things for themselves because he himself wants them, but because others possess them. When he finally reaches his goal, he often derives a mere satisfaction of momentary vanity instead of positive and lasting happiness. Mechanics can produce beautiful machines; it can also deform humanity.[4]

Every invention is extraordinary in itself: its con-

[3] These lines, it should be remembered, were written before 1939. P. L. N.
[4] Samuel Butler, as far back as 1868, foresaw this in his remarkably clever and brilliant book *Erewhon*.

sequences are often tragic. I allude not only to material consequences, accidents of all kinds, but also to moral consequences. Men are chained to the wheel and seek their joys solely in immediate pleasures. They think only of participating in the whirlwind that envelops them and of escaping from themselves. Their greatest tragedy is to be alone, face to face with themselves, with nothing to do. People reach the point where they cannot bear silence. Radios blare out all day. If people leave their homes, it is only to go to the movies. Noise, excitement of any kind, at any price, to keep from thinking. The effect on children is disastrous, for they lose that habit of playing by themselves which develops imagination. Ambitions are more and more limited to those mediocre pleasures that are depicted as the perfect ideal to be attained. Thus for the great majority of men, life, real life, passes by without touching them and without their even noticing it.

Certain improvements of science, applied without discernment by industrialists whose business it is to make money or by governments blinded by primary economic concepts, do not take into account the nature of man, nor his deeper interests. But that is not all. It is not always true that governments are blind. They are sometimes led by formidable ambitions that can only be realized by wholesale lies that lead, as in Germany and Russia, to slavery and war.

It must be admitted that science, which is the foundation of everything we call progress, incurs a grave responsibility in all this. But I deem it my duty, as a scientist, to protest against the intellectual swindle that has tried to use science as an accomplice and has attempted thus to justify an absurd philosophy and a form of government hostile to human dignity and freedom.

There remains pure science, the science that "enables us to seek the truth." The first part of this book was consecrated to the study of this truth, and to the means by which we can arrive at a knowledge of it. What are the conclusions? On first analysis, the clearest profit that we have derived from pure science is represented by a limited knowledge of the relations between certain external mechanisms. These relations are only known to us by the succession of our reactions to phenomena. We know that we are totally ignorant of the very nature of these mechanisms, as we can only imagine them by the help of subjective, physiological reactions. On further analysis, we see that all the observed mechanisms are of a statistical nature and only represent, on our scale of observation, the resultant of an immense number of elementary phenomena, on a microscopic and sub-microscopic scale. Finally, we perceive that there is an uncertainty in the universe that must be mathematically incorporated in the formulae required to describe our world—an uncertainty that rigorously limits our prevision of the future.

We are incapable of linking the properties of bodies to those of the constituent particles; of defining the difference between life and death; of explaining the origin of life; of understanding the mechanisms of evolution. Half a century ago, people thought that the solution of these problems was comparatively easy and needed but a little time. Many scientists treated them as already solved. The fact that we admit our ignorance is proof that we have progressed; we know that we do not know.

To this day, science has not succeeded in eliminating the hypothesis of an "anti-chance," which it is simpler to call God. In all honesty, we are forced to recognize that we face the same point that Pascal posed when he made his famous wager.[5] What is more, if we should bet we would have more arguments in favor of his choice than Pascal himself had. Without making a great effort of intelligence, without even contemplating the disturbing problems that we have touched upon in this book, and without casting any judgment, we must at least admit that from a logical point of view the "hypothesis God" has not been weakened by science since Pascal's time. In truth, if we refuse to admit a dualism, if we espouse the old materialistic thesis and if, following Bertrand Russell and several other lesser men, we only recognize chance as the ultimate and unique cause, then we must necessarily admit that we have chosen this solution by chance and that, consequently, there is one chance out of two that we have made a mistake.

What will happen, then, to the prestige of science, on which people counted so much to smother and replace the prestige of religion? What will become of those who exploited science to satisfy their personal ambition and their animosity against spiritual authority? The weapon which they forged and polished with love, in which they placed all their hopes, has turned against them. They must defend themselves at all costs. Since science has always remained aloof from the crowd and

[5] Either God exists or He does not exist. There is no middle ground. Reason is impotent to help us to decide. A game of infinite consequence is being played in which heads or tails must win. We must gamble. We have no choice. Not to wager that God exists is to wager that He does not exist. Which side will we take? We have two things to lose: truth and goodness. But also at stake are our intellect and our aspirations—knowledge and eternal happiness. Our nature abhors two things: error and sorrow. Therefore why hesitate to gamble that God exists? Choose you must. The impact upon your mind will be equally severe, no matter which choice you make. That point is obvious. But what of the possibility of your eternal happiness? If you choose to believe, you gain all if you win—and you lose nothing if you lose. Therefore, believe—if you can.   PASCAL (condensed from the French)

since the average man cannot judge for himself, it becomes necessary to ridicule "dangerous" interpretations,
to lie, if need be, and to neglect or dissimulate embarrassing
facts and theories. They must create a new mysticism of
science, introduce sentiment, speak to man the language
he understands, awake the faith that lies dormant in him,
and orient him in a new direction by taking up again the
old revolutionary methods.

But the Goddess of Reason is bankrupt; the religion of
positivism has foundered; and they are forced to fall back
on an old-fashioned philosophy: Hegel's spiritualistic
dialectics. They simply replace the word "spiritualistic"
by the word "materialistic." The work of demarcation was
done many years ago by the "apostles" of anarchism. A
few holes are filled with putty, a layer of varnish is put on,
and finally there emerges the most absurd doctrine that
was ever produced by the human brain—a veritable de-
fiance of intelligence and of science: the materialistic
dialectics of the Soviets. We must not forget that technical
periodicals have published articles such as: "The Dialectics
of the Internal Combustion Engine," "The Dialectics of
Synchronous Machines," "The Dialectics of Steel Alloys,"
and "For the Purity of the Marxist-Leninist Theory in
Surgery." [6]

I hope the reader will excuse the emotion that underlies
these lines. The reason of it is given by Pascal, who writes
in his *Pensées:* "How is it that we have so much patience
with those who are lame in body and so little with those
who are lame in mind? Because the lame man recognizes
that we walk straight, but the lame mind maintains that
it is we who limp. Were it not so, we should feel pity and

[6] See: "Pravda," June 4, 1932, article by Setzki; see also L. Rougier,
"La Mystique Soviétique," Brussels, 1936.

not anger." I am willing to admit that, strange as it may seem, the "lame mind" is sometimes sincere. But if it is, what a regression since Lobatchewsky, Mendéléeff and Pavlov!

Let us make no mistake: pure science is magnificent and more than any other manifestation of human activity deserves an unbounded admiration. But the human brain that created it is really what we should admire.

Neither scientists nor philosophers foresaw the consequences of science, which are not always without danger. Hypnotized by the joy of discovery, intoxicated by their present success that gave hopes of greater successes to come, they never asked themselves what use would be made of them. They did not think of the immense power that would be placed in the hands of men whose ambitions are not limited to the discovery of a new element, or to the study of leprosy, and to ten or twelve hours per day of badly paid and often risky work in a laboratory. The danger of pure science does not lie in science itself but in the interpretations and theories. Intellectual value does not necessarily go hand in hand with moral value. The utilization made of certain discoveries and certain hypotheses is a proof of this. A doctor's diploma guarantees neither the intelligence nor the morality of its holder.

In this book I have tried to show that though the observations of science are solid its interpretations are sometimes fragile. My sole aim in doing this was to warn laymen against the scientific mysticism that does not withstand an honest examination but that some people have tried to turn into a weapon against spiritual mysticism. Scientific superstition, like all superstitions, derives its prestige in part from the ignorance of the crowd. It must not be allowed to keep a free man from thinking freely.

As a social lever, science is an ideal tool. It is in fashion: a boxer, a tennis player, are called scientific. Science adds the attraction of mystery to that of intellectual pursuits. For the immense majority of the public, today's laboratory is not very different, in principle, from that of the alchemist. Visitors often give the impression that they are looking for the stuffed crocodile hanging from the ceiling. It is always easy to deceive people when they have no means of control. The language of modern science is an incomprehensible jargon for the average man. Scientists themselves do not always agree on the significance of words. But the less we understand, the more easily are we convinced. The passage from the rational to the sentimental realm occurs with remarkable facility, and quite unconsciously. A few amoral individuals, followed by a great number of simple minds, could not resist the temptation of seizing the opportunity to make science say things that pleased them sentimentally, or that could, eventually, be of use to them. Science could not defend itself.

It is because of this fact that the true crisis is a moral crisis—for it rests on lies. If these men would consent to say to the crowd: "We have been mistaken; we know nothing"; if governments dared to reveal the true reasons for their actions, and if people were better informed on the conditions of life and popular sentiment in other countries, it is infinitely probable that the world would not be in its present hysterical condition. But is it not a hopeless task to attempt to suppress untruth? "Speech has been given man to disguise his thoughts"; and man talks without cease. . . .

The "opiate of the people" was much advertised. It is a magnificent slogan. Those who first made use of it may have been sincere. Unless a person is congenitally feeble-minded, or ignorant, it is difficult to believe that anyone would claim that this is the case today. The fact that the progress of science has enabled them to replace the opiate by cocaine and morphine seems to indicate that they are not dangerous through stupidity. We must hope that enough courage and intelligence will soon be found on earth to enable men to forget for a while their purely personal and economic interests, and so to help them understand that the civilization in which they take so much pride will collapse unless it rests on more solid foundations.

RECAPITULATION AND CONCLUSION

Argument

There is the same difference between our science and that of our grandparents as there is between Whistler and a surrealist painter. The atom and electron of 1910 no more corresponded to reality than the period itself corresponded to normal. Today's electron is also the picture of our times; it offers no security, and changes from day to day. The problems solved by science have led to others that are even more complicated. The answers of science can only be mathematical.

Man is more than a combination of appetites, instincts, passions and curiosity. He has had and still has the choice of two different roads. The one is superficially easy since it considers the material world as the only reality. The other requires a rigorous discipline and admits the reality of imponderable spiritual forces. Can we not find a middle road, the Road to Reason, on which both science and religion can meet and work together for the creation of a spiritually and physically perfect man?

8

RECAPITULATION AND CONCLUSION

In the hour of affliction, scientific knowledge will
not console us for our ignorance of moral values.
But the knowledge of moral qualities will always
console us when faced by material considerations.
—PASCAL

PHYSICISTS of the 19th century had drawn a picture of
the universe that was as satisfactory and reassuring as
today's picture is unsatisfactory. There is the same difference between our science and that of our grandparents
as there is between a cubist or surrealist painting and a
Meissonnier or a Whistler. The small indivisible balls,
which we fondly dreamed represented atoms, gave way at
first to minute solar systems in which the electrons were
the planets. To explain the discontinuity of energy, it then
became necessary to allow the electrons to jump from one
orbit to another. At that time they were considered as
particles of matter but with a mass dependent on their
velocity, which was most disturbing. When moving to an
outside orbit a quantum of energy was absorbed; when
passing from the outside to inner orbits a quantum was
emitted. It was admitted that eight electrons could occupy
an orbit. The central nucleus—the "sun"—1840 times

heavier than the electron, carried a positive charge that maintained the electrons (negative electric particles) on their orbits. This model was certainly not ideal and raised many difficulties of detail (for example, the rotation of an electron on an orbit was supposed to entail neither absorption nor emission of energy, which is not very clear). But it had become familiar and in spite of its complexity we considered it as a friend; we had begun to forget its imperfections. It was, after all, "conceivable," and there was something reassuring in the fact that there existed only one ultimate element that was the same for matter and electricity. We had no sooner become accustomed to it, I might almost say attached to it, than we learned rather brutally that this atom was only an impostor and that the real atom had never resembled such a monster. We were told that there were not only two elements, the electron and the proton, but at least three, one positive and one, the neutron which carries no charge; the mesons, positive and negative; the photon, quantum of light, which like the particles is constituted of energy; and two entities whose reality is limited to the necessity for balancing equations, the neutrino and antineutrino, actually bookkeeping particles. Furthermore, only one electron can occupy an orbit, and today we can hardly even speak of an orbit. We cannot even talk about an electron, in the sense that we did a few years ago, for the electron is at the same time a particle—perhaps deprived of mass—and a wave. Strictly speaking, it is not even a particle; it is only the expression of the probability that the properties that we attribute to the electron are to be found in a certain point of space. To be clearer, we can say that the electron is a wave of probability. The current notions of time and space no longer apply to these entities, which evolve in a pluri-dimensional, non-Euclidean space. Ten electrons move in a thirty-dimensional space.

All those who are old enough to have appreciated the charm of life before the war of 1914 will understand why certain physicists long for the atom and the electron of 1910. They no more corresponded to reality than the period itself corresponded to normal. Today's electron is also the picture of our times. It offers no guarantee of security. It does not exist in our perceptible universe and is not subject to the same laws. No one can say how long it will last. It will have evolved between the day these lines are written and the day they appear in print—and may no longer resemble the sketch I have just drawn of it! *

Yet this is the ultimate element that is at the disposal of the physicist to create physics, of the chemist to understand chemistry, of the biologist to understand life, and of the philosopher to explain thought. The task is difficult, for as long as the very foundation of our universe rests on such fragile concepts the problem of life cannot receive a satisfactory answer. All the problems that science has solved so far have only led to the discovery of others that were unsuspected until then and that are increasingly complex. Mathematical language is the only language that can be applied in the realm of physics but, at present, physics as a whole cannot be interpreted by one geometry —and physics is extremely simple when compared to biology.

Progress is rapid. But our actual science rests on the corpses of so many outworn theories, of so many illusions, that we must show the greatest circumspection when attempting a philosophical extrapolation. Only working

* EDITOR'S NOTE: Since these lines were written our picture of the atom and its components has become still more complicated.

hypotheses are legitimate and without danger when we seek to give an interpretation of the universe—an interpretation that can no longer be anything but mathematical. If we admit the reality of modern physics—and it seems difficult to escape this obligation—we must completely abandon all hope of a mechanical interpretation.

If the goal is ever attained, if the total mathematical explanation of the world is achieved, man will find himself faced by a system in which the universe will be represented by groups of equations, by ratios, and a few numbers. These symbols, born of his brain, will form a conceptual coherent whole and will enable him to describe and foresee, by calculation, all the events of the external world—namely, the quantitative elements of the states of consciousness that are the result of a qualitative sensation or an emotion. We shall have to rely upon a purely empirical procedure, however, in order to account for the qualitative element directly perceived (mass for example), or for relations of quality, such as the harmony of certain colors or of certain sounds. This would tend to prove that the mathematical concept was not complete. As to aesthetic, moral, or abstract ideas, it is clear that they cannot enter into the picture; the first two, because they belong entirely to the realm of quality; the last, because they are the result of the transformation of the immediate perceptions of consciousness and therefore are directly derived from them in a way that is unknown.

The image of the world will then be formed of numbers, of ratios between readings on a dial, which will allow the prevision of other dial readings as a function of the variations shown on still other dials.

To say that this solution is entirely satisfactory would be an exaggeration. Obviously it only tends to be descriptive, which is in accord with the ambition of science. But it is incomplete since it does not take into account the thought of man nor the processes that started from qualitative sensations, and translated them into a different symbolical language. Human thought is an integral part of the universe, of the cosmos, and any explanation that neglects this element of the problem cannot pretend to be general, but remains relative and arbitrary. Looked at from a purely pragmatic, utilitarian angle, the scheme is satisfactory. Unfortunately, certain scientists who profess to scorn philosophy and to despise metaphysics think that they can suppress the objects of metaphysics by showing that these objects—God and the soul amongst others—have no place in this concept. This argument may convince them but it seems less than conclusive to others. For, after all, this system was begotten by them, or, if not by them, by other human minds. It would be surprising indeed if a quantity that had not been introduced into a mathematical construction were contained in it. Nothing can be drawn from a reasoning of this kind, or from a syllogism, that did not already exist in the original equations, in the postulates, or in the premises. It is conceivable that these scientists should have faith in this structural scheme or in its future. But to lean on it in order to create a negative metaphysics is simply an error of reasoning. We should not blame them for reasoning falsely when dealing with non-scientific matters, for that is not their field and the result can only harm themselves. But when they abuse the prestige that their purely technical work has given them and attempt to spread these ideas among the young, one is justified in criticizing their anti-scientific spirit and in deploring the fact that their arguments contain elements of passion that no more belong in the embryo of the mathematical scheme

234 • THE ROAD TO REASON

they defend than do the convictions they reproach others
for having.

Man is not merely a combination of appetites, instincts,
passions, and curiosity. Something more is needed to explain great human deeds, virtues, sacrifices, martyrdom.
There is an element in the great mystics, the saints, the
prophets, whose influence has been felt for centuries, which
escapes mere intelligence. We do not admit physical
miracles, because they are outside the actual framework
of our knowledge; yet we admit the reality of Joan of Arc,
who represents a real and confounding miracle.

We cannot ask science to raise the moral level of
humanity. The present state of the world is proof enough
that this is an illusion. Must we then, as Renan thought,
return to the "myths" that had produced such a surprising
result in the case of the kindhearted gorilla? Is it true, as
Renan said, that "the downfall of idealistic beliefs is
destined to follow the downfall of supernatural beliefs,
and that a real abasement of the morals of humanity dates
from the day in which it saw the reality of things"?

If this is the case, would we not be justified in demanding
the return of the "myths" that differentiated man from the
animals, rather than submit to this abasement, which "is
absolutely repugnant"? The life of the anthill is not suited
to living beings who can boast of noble lives, magnificent
gestures, generous and disinterested acts, moral grandeur,
artistic and intellectual masterpieces—proving to man
that, after all, there is a difference between himself and
the Neanderthal man.

What man should be proudest of is precisely the fact
that he has given birth, from time to time, to beings who
live on a higher plane than himself. Who can say if that

is not precisely his role in the universe? Science teaches us that though our laws are statistical laws in which the individual particle plays no part, it is possible that the particles which escape the statistical laws in living beings are the ones which determine and orient the evolution that we observe but do not understand. Can we not conceive two degrees in the universe? The first corresponds to the material world, the realm of energy, of the first and of the second principle of thermodynamics, of macroscopic determinism, leading to more and more probable states of equilibrium. The second corresponds to the world of spiritual forces, bringing only minute quantities of energy into play but capable of orienting indetermination in a definite direction and no longer only in "the most probable direction."

Moreover, how can we explain the fact that these myths are the only food transformed by man into moral values, into beauty? Is not this a proof of their reality? The coupling of the latter word to that of "myths" may seem shocking, but what is left today of that Reality which, according to Renan, should alone suffice to smother these myths on which philosophers attempted to build a temple? In the course of this book we have seen that this reality consists entirely of groups of equations without material support and only valid in a space and time different from ours; of "waves of probability." Myth for myth, is it not unwise and anti-scientific to deny *a priori* the relative existence of the one that produces tangible results unobtainable by the other? Why should the law of causality, so dear to the materialists, cease to apply precisely in this case? The phenomenon that interests us in connection with man is what differentiates him from the animal; on the one hand, his power of creating, his faculty of abstraction;

on the other, his moral value, symbolized by his idealism, his sense of duty, his respect for the concepts of goodness, justice, and virtue. We do not know what determines the creative and abstractive powers, but we know, empirically, what produces the others.

We face a conflict that Socrates had already perceived —we need only read *Phaedo* to be convinced of this—and that had struck Leibnitz. The discoveries and theories of modern physics have only deepened it. The science of yesterday, or rather, a few philosophers nurtured on science, thought that a clean sweep of everything that was not forces and atoms could be made with impunity. It considered these were the sole realities. We have learned that, with respect to us, atoms only acquire their reality through their velocities and accelerations. This is essentially the foundation of our materialism. Who will dare affirm, today, that this alone enables us to attain the joy of living and the formation of the superior conscience of which Renan speaks?

Though it is impossible to arrest what we call material progress, which by itself apparently cannot assure the happiness of the individual, the satisfaction of all his aspirations, and the development of his moral being; though it may be impossible to go against the stream; yet it is to be hoped that the moral education of children from their earliest childhood will retain the attention of nations as much, indeed even more, than their intellectual education. Nobody would think of making a fine embroidery on weak or rotten material. The only way in which we can progress is to prepare a firm canvas, worthy of the design that will enrich it; that is, to build up generations endowed with strong physical and moral health. It may be that Renan was right—and that the only way to prepare these morally strong and noble generations is to have recourse to religion, which he admits we cannot do without.[1]

Man has had the choice between two roads to happiness. The one is smooth and satisfies that thirst for knowledge, that curiosity—*libido scienti*—to which we owe our science. It is an easy, agreeable road, favorable to all appetites and rich in benefits of every kind. The other is hard, painful, thankless, without tangible profits; it requires a rigorous discipline, unceasing mortifications, and treats the body as an enemy. The only reality recognized by the first is the material world. The second, on the contrary, admits as an important reality only imponderable spiritual forces. The first road seemed to be the most logical one, and rightly so, as long as we could believe in the existence of a simple material reality, of a solid and *conceivable* basis to our universe. It is natural that a certain elite should have chosen it. Analytical sense, pure intelligence, found ample sustenance in the harvest of experimental facts that were lacking in the second one.

But when it was realized—it was not really so long ago—that the ponderable was formed of the imponderable and that beyond the order and harmony of the world man only discovered disorder and chaos, then the question arose if, after all, the second road did not correspond to a reality as deep as that which our unaided intelligence can con-

---

[1] Adopting a pragmatic point of view, Emile Borel writes: "I know that certain people (Le Dantec) think that the knowledge of supreme truth, that is, the belief in absolute determinism and in the epiphenomenal consciousness, will result in making the life of humanity impossible. If this is so, it is a reason for doubting this supreme truth, for it would be the first example of the nefarious influence of truth on human evolution. Those who believe in a rigorously materialistic determinism would be logical with themselves in having no aversion for lies, whose social value appears incontestable: so long as these lies are momentarily useful, they should be respected and propagated." (*Loc. cit.*, p. 229.)

ceive; or if truth did not lie in a combination of the two roads. Indeed, man is a whole. His activities are strictly interdependent. They are the consequences, under divers aspects, of his physiological reactions but, on the other hand, his physiological activity depends, in part, on his nervous system and on his affective life, his emotions. Love acts on the sexual glands; fear on the suprarenal and the sweat-producing glands; a cretin is generally a being whose thyroid gland functions badly.

Every man, at a given period of his life, may be characterized in very different ways: from an anatomical point of view; from a physiological, pathological, chemical, and physico-chemical point of view; from an aesthetic, moral, social, and even sentimental angle. Any portrait that takes into account only one of these sides, even if it is altogether accurate, is necessarily incomplete. It resembles the photographs of the sun taken with spectral rays of sodium or hydrogen. And yet we often judge people on fragmentary pictures of this kind. But all these portraits, like photographs of a monument taken from the interior, the exterior, and from every possible angle, are the resultant of one single complex phenomenon: *that* man.

The reactions of that man, in the intellectual, as well as on the moral and purely physical plane, are always the echo of the biological, physical, and chemical reactions of which his body is, or has been, the seat; and the contrary is true. This is factual, independent of any hypothesis. The whole constitutes a definite unit resulting from this perfect and necessary correlation. It is still impossible to separate any of these activities arbitrarily without impairing the unity of the individual, for nobody knows exactly how these various functions influence each other. The emotions react directly on the economy of the body and bring about chemical reactions through the intermediary of the nervous system. The origin of moral ideas, as that of instincts, entirely escapes us. We deduce their existence from their effects, just as we do for electrons. But these effects have a physiological, material counterpart.

It is clear that neither of these two tendencies that confront each other—on the one hand, absolute deterministic materialism, and on the other, absolute spiritualism—represents a complete comprehensive and human outlook, looking upon man as a unit. Neither the one nor the other contains a practical solution to the social problem or to the moral problem, for they each take into consideration only half of the human being, not man as a whole. As I said before, it is perhaps through a combination of the two points of view, and with a less intolerant, more scientific attitude, that the sociologist, the statesman, and the director of consciences must in the future consider the problem.

Man is a whole, we repeat, and his immense complexity results in the most fundamental unity of nature. He is subject to the laws of a world that he dominates by his thought. Above thought, which produces abstract ideas, there are the moral and spiritual forces, creators of virtue and hope. We do not know how to link either of them to the material whole from which they spring. But we cannot deny their existence. They play a preponderant role in our social and private life. They are responsible for the progressive ascension of man in nature. The accumulation of many new facts has relegated these ideas to the bottom of our consciousness. We have progressively allowed them to slip out of our habitual preoccupations, because we have deceived ourselves on the universality of science, which, being our creation, satisfied our pride. We have forgotten that science limits itself to describing, interpreting, and predicting material phenomena, revealed by our senses. We have overlooked, behind the codified and conquered material forces, the directing forces that alone characterize man. We have looked solely for the things that connect him with brute matter and animals; we have lost interest in those that raise him above them. Yet this difference inspires the sentiment of that dignity which is inseparable from the unit we call Man. We had hoped that the transition between unorganized matter and thought was progressive. If this is so, we are still far from being able to prove it; if we wait to be sure of it before giving our attention to the moral factors of our evolution, we can be certain that it will be too late, and that this civilization of which we boast will have disappeared from the surface of the globe.

We did not wait to understand the nature of electricity before building dynamos and factories. Had we done so, we would have no electric force, light, or telegraph today. It is no longer a question of increasing our comfort but of saving the house built with so much labor—that house whose very foundations are tottering. To accomplish this, there is only one method: it is to consider man, in his complexity, as a single problem and to cease separating instruction from moral education. This implies the collaboration of all those who specialize in the study and development of the human being, from a physical and intellectual point of view. We cannot hope to correct and adapt the sad heritage of the last century. We must therefore turn toward the future and model a new youth—rich in ideals, liberated from pseudophilosophical impostures, strengthened by an unalloyed science, respectful of its mission, and capable of transmitting the flickering torch to future generations.

INDEX

Absolute beginning, 49, 140, 145, 152, 175, 188–89
Absolute first cause, 73, 74
Acetylcholine, 49
Adaptation, chemical, 164–67
    to microbic infections, 164
    theory of, *see* Lamarck
Adrenalin, 49
Adsorption, 131–32
Agnosticism, 20
Albumin, 127, 128, 153 n., 165
Amiel, Henri Frédéric, 96
Amino acids, molecular weights, 127–28
Amoebae, 131, 136, 137
Analysis, 35, 41, 68, 95
    combinatorial, 147
    limitations of, 55
    outstanding scientific method, 47–48
Anatomy, 51
Anderson, Carl David, 80
Angstrom unit, 57
Antibody and antigen, 165
Antichance ("Maxwell's demon"), 111 n., 113, 126, 130, 139, 156, 183, 195, 221
Antineutrino, 230
Arcturus, ray from, 71
Aristotle, 27
Arrhenius, Svante, 78, 80
Assimilation, 131, 136
Astronomical distances, expressed in microns, 121–22
Atheism, 19–20
Atom: creation of, 153
    energy of quantum of, 31

Atom—*cont'd*
    picture of, recent changes in, 229–31, 236
    properties of, 50
    extreme smallness of, 121
Atomic theory, 30 n., 86, 110, 141
Atoms, 31, 51, 86, 108, 123, 126, 143, 145, 147, 174, 229
    as individuals, causal relations with elementary particles, 175
Avery, Oswald Theodore, 165

Balmer rays, 52
Balzac, Honoré de, 198
Banting, Sir Frederic G., 80
Beginning, absolute, *see* Absolute beginning
Behaviorism, 192
Bergson, Henri, 19, 109
Bernard, Claude, 80
Bernouilli, Daniel, 86
Berthelot, P. E. M., 30 n., 80
Berthollet, Claude Louis, 89
Bertrand, Joseph, 87, 141
Bible, 107
Biochemistry, 51, 145
Biology, 50, 145, 189, 231
    inadequacy of second principle of thermodynamics applied to, 56–57
Bohr, Niels, 80
Boltzmann, Ludwig, 73–74, 98, 105, 134
Borel, Emile, 33, 66, 75–76, 113, 115–19
    quoted, 142–43, 146 n., 154, 188–89

241

Hunger, 199
Huxley, Thomas Henry, "organized
    common sense," 31 n., 35
Hydrogen, 49
Hypothesis: born of imagination,
        77–81
    definition of, 77
    fundamental tool of science, 77–
        81
    useful though false, 59, 78, 87
    value of, 59

Ice, crystal of, growth or fusion, 88
Ideological motives, of crowd, 199
Imagination, 59
    creative, smothered by education,
        79
    most fruitful years for, 80–81
    need for, 76–77
    pioneer work of scientists with,
        78–81, 160
    source of hypotheses, 77–81
Immunity, 8, 163–67
Impossibility ("high improbabil-
        ity"), 93, 116, 124
Indeterminacy, Heisenberg's princi-
        ple of, 42, 157, 175–78, 183
Indians, lack of immunity, 164
Individual: cell, formation of, 132–
        33
    in physics and biology, 113, 150,
        151
    suppressed in subatomic realm,
        113
Individual, in human society, 196,
        201, 234–35
    part played in evolution by, 155,
        234–35
    pioneer in science, 9, 195
    struggle for power by, 195, 201–
        26
Inertia, 57
Infrared rays, 57, 58

Inorganic chemistry, 51, 135–37
Insects, metamorphosis of, 41
    society of, 188, 201
Instincts, value of, 183
Insulin, 65
Insurance, statistical calculations,
        65, 154
Intelligence, 53, 58, 112, 145, 189–
        90, 237
    civilization created by, 75
    divinity of, 208
    unequal distribution of, 79
Interpolation, 56
Interpretation, statistical, see Statis-
        tical interpretation
Ions, 78, 138
Irreversibility of phenomena, 83,
        88–89
    of cell growth, 136
    correlated with probability, ex-
        periment, 88–94, 99
    linked to second principle of
        thermodynamics, 96–99

Jeans, Sir James, 116–17
Joan of Arc, 234
Joliot, Frédéric, 80

Kant, Immanuel, "Third Antin-
        omy," 73
Katabolism, 131
Kelvin, Lord, 30 n.
Kepler, Johannes, 157, 160
Kinetic energy, of falling body, 95
Kinetic theory: of electronic con-
        ductivity, 66
    of gases, 66–68, 86, 169, 183
Knowledge: diffusion of, 209
    problems of, 76–77
    vs. imagination, 77

Lacape, R. S., 48
Lachelier, Jules, 47